BUSINESS ENG

AN INDIVIDUALISED LEARNING PRO

PETER WILBERG   MICHAEL LEWIS

LTP
35 Church Road Hove BN3 2BE
Tel 0273-736344
Fax 0273-720898

ISBN   Bound edition   0 906717 72 8
       Looseleaf edition   0 906717 97 3
       Teachers' Manual   0 906717 80 9
       Assessment (pack)   0 906717 96 5

Printed in England by Commercial Colour Press, London E7.

Business English is based on an idea by Peter Wilberg. The materials have been developed
by Peter Wilberg and Michael Lewis. The cross-cultural material was contributed by Philip
O'Connor of Language Training Services in consultation with Michael Lewis.

Acknowledgements

We are grateful for permission to reproduce the newspaper articles on pages 48 and 92.
The front cover was designed by Deb Durban, based on a picture from the Zefa Picture
Library (UK).

Copyright

CONTENTS

HOW TO GET THE BEST OUT OF YOUR COURSE AND THIS BOOK

On these two pages are some general guidance to help you learn efficiently and effectively.

1. Set yourself objectives before you begin your course. Decide what you need to learn. Make a plan. How much time can you give each day/week to improving your English?

2. **Either** follow the plan **or** change it, but **don't** forget it. Approach improving your English in the same way you approach a carefully designed project at work:

set objectives   make a timetable   review progress   revise objectives

3. Remember, a lot of your work will be wasted if you do not keep a good record of what you learn. Record the new language you need **accurately** and in a way that you can **recover** the information. The carefully designed pages of this book will help you to organise what you learn so that you can find the language you need later.

4. Remember, it is a waste of time to record information unless you can find it again when you need it. A list of **all** the new words from your English class is often almost useless, because you will not be able to find the word you need a few weeks later!

5. It is difficult to remember things arranged in lists (try to learn a few lines of the telephone book!). It is better to arrange the new words and phrases you learn in other ways, which make them easier to remember. This book suggests some effective ways of arranging new language.

6. It is easier to remember new language if you write a sentence which uses the new word. It is even better if the sentence is your own personal sentence. Choose one which is true, about yourself or a friend, or perhaps an amusing sentence. All these ways will help you to remember the new words better.

7. After you have written your sentences, say them aloud. Say them more than once, until they seem natural to you. It is important that you feel happy when you say the new sentences. That helps you to remember better, too.

8. When you feel natural with a new sentence, say it once again. This time record it, in your own voice, on a cassette tape. Later, when you are doing nothing — perhaps when you are driving your car — listen to the tape. Many people learn very efficiently by listening to their own voices!

9. When you are working with your teacher, don't worry about making mistakes. When you make a mistake it helps the teacher to help you. It is very difficult to help students who worry too much about making mistakes.

10. Not all mistakes are very important. Mistakes are important if somebody mis-understands what you mean, or if somebody thinks you are rude or aggressive when you do not mean to be. Some mistakes are important to **you** because they make you feel silly. If you think a mistake is important make a careful note of it (see pages 120 to 126) and then make a special effort to avoid those mistakes later.

11. One of the best ways to improve is for you to **try to say** what you want, and then for your teacher to tell you the **best** way of saying that naturally. When your teacher helps you like this, write down the **exact** words, then look back regularly until you are confident that you can use the natural language yourself.

12. This book should be a record of **all the important language you learn** on your course. That should make it very valuable. Take care of it and use it regularly!

CLASSROOM ENGLISH

Many people who are studying business English are studying it with a teacher, either alone or in a small group. These classes provide a real opportunity to practise English which is important in real business situations. You can use the classroom like a business meeting — not like a classroom. Forget that there is a 'teacher' and 'students'; instead, think of all the people as participants in a business meeting. Both the teacher and the student(s) should use the language in class which is normally used in business. Treat the class as a meeting and practise interrupting, changing the subject, asking for more details etc. using businesslike language. Here are some useful expressions:

Shall we begin by looking at....
I wonder if it might be helpful/a good idea to....

Would you like me to go over that again/in more detail?
Could you go over that again/in more detail, please?

Are you sure?
Really?
Could you be more specific?

I'm not sure I completely understand/agree.
I wonder if that's the best way/if there's a better way of doing that.

Excuse me, could I just ask a question/make a point before you/we go on?
I think we'd better leave that until a later/our next meeting.
I'm not sure this is the right time to discuss that question.

I'll let you have a summary of what we have said today/tomorrow/in a few days.
Do you think you could just let me have a few notes about what we've said today please.

otice all this language is like the language of a business meeting, not the language of a language lesson! Use your lessons to practise for meetings.

LEARNING ENGLISH

Nobody is quite sure how we learn. Some people seem to learn best in one way and other people in a different way. But there are some general principles which will help you. Often in this book you will find expert help. There are short notes which will make your studying more effective. They look like this:

Don't just list every new word you meet. Choose words you think are important for you.

Don't just list one form of a word; make sure you know the family of words:

      produce (verb)   product (noun)   production (noun)
      productivity (noun)   producer (noun)

Try to make an example sentence about your job or your own life for each of the words in the word family. This will help you to remember them better.

IDENTIFYING YOUR NEEDS

There are two important steps to improving your English for professional reasons.

1. Identifying the language you need.

2. Recording what you learn in the most effective way.

Before you begin, you need to think about these things carefully. In business you plan before you do anything. You want to avoid wasting time, money and work. It is the same with your foreign language study. You need to plan, to set yourself clear objectives, and to work in an organised, efficient and effective way. Planning is not wasting time. It is an important part of your study programme.

This book helps you to discover your language needs and objectives. After you have done that, it helps if you study effectively and record what you learn in the most useful way. This first section of the book is very important. It is designed to help you to plan your learning programme. Use it carefully. Don't rush. It will help you to discover the things which it is most important and helpful for you to learn. Take your time. You are making an important investment!

Fill in the tables on the next few pages. If you can, do this in English. You can also complete them in your own language. It is more important to complete these pages fully and accurately, than to do it in English. These pages are not to test your English. They are to help you, and your teacher, to discover the English you need.

1

NEEDS 1 — TOPICS

Complete the table below as fully as possible. Use your own language or English or both. Use the ideas at the top of the page to help you, but think carefully of **why** you need English and **how** you need to use English. Think of your job and of yourself, and your personal needs and interests.

I NEED ENGLISH FOR:

banking   sales   finance   meeting visitors

import/export   accountancy   advertising

?   ?

personnel management   economics   retail trade   agriculture

?

travel   ?   computers   entertaining

NEED	DETAILS
1	
2	
3	
4	
5	

NEEDS 2 — FUNCTIONS

Which of these things do you need to do in English? Give as many details as possible. Remember, you can use English or your own language.

I NEED TO DO THESE THINGS IN ENGLISH:

greet visitors   suggestion   make small talk   discuss proposals
                      make a complaint   contracts
? express my opinion   request   agree and disagree   problems

          present my company   describe people
    graphs   our product   plans
talk about figures   our plans   ?   jobs   talk on the phone
    money   products
                                           places   interrupt

    answer questions   compare things

NEED	DETAILS
Things I do often in English	
1	
2	
3	
I don't do it often, but it is very important.	
Something special I am going to do soon in English.	

1

NEEDS 3 — SITUATIONS

If you want to discover the language you need it will help if you think about the different situations when you use English. The language you need changes from place to place and from person to person. Use the suggested words to help to describe as carefully as possible when and where you use English.

WHO DO YOU SPEAK ENGLISH TO?	clients customers colleagues technicians responsibility superiors secretarial staff bosses nationality ????
WHAT ABOUT?	products arrangements plans deals prices discounts promotions supplies
WHY?	reporting buying agreeing selling discussing reviewing presenting introducing
WHERE AND WHEN?	country place factory office conference trade fair meeting social contacts
HOW DO YOU USE ENGLISH?	telephone face-to-face one-to-one groups meetings in writing telex ????
HOW DO YOU MEET ENGLISH REGULARLY?	private reading company literature TV radio professional press contact with native English/American speakers

NEEDS 4 — DAILY ROUTINE

Think about how you spend a typical day. Fill in things which you do regularly. Use English as much as possible; use your own language if necessary. This diary page might help you to think of more occasions when you use English for your job. Use the suggestions to help you. Underline all the things you do in English.

A TYPICAL DAY

Morning	Lunch time	Afternoon	Evening

YESTERDAY

Morning	Lunch time	Afternoon	Evening

analysing .....   meeting .....   planning .....   explaining .....   listening to .....

phoning .....   arranging .....   liaising with .....   checking .....   visiting .....

socialising with .....   instructing .....   thinking about .....   interviewing .....   relaxing .....

reviewing .....   consulting .....   writing .....   negotiating .....   travelling .....

Which five activities on this list do you do most often in English?

1

NEEDS 5 — ANNUAL ROUTINE

Probably your job changes at different times of year. But most of us operate an annual cycle; things happen regularly at the same time of year. Use the year planner below to list regular events in your calendar. Underline the ones when you use English. Does it help you to discover more of your language needs?

JANUARY

FEBRUARY

MARCH

APRIL

MAY

JUNE

NEEDS 6 — ANNUAL ROUTINE

JULY

AUGUST

SEPTEMBER

OCTOBER

NOVEMBER

DECEMBER

Think of all the national holidays that you have in your own country. Fill them in on the calendar in English. Here are some of the expressions you may need

New Years Day	**Easter**	**Christmas**
Annual Holidays	**May Day**	**Religious Holiday**

The more detail you put on your calendar, the more it will help you to think of situations when you use your English. The calendar can help you and your teacher to identify more of your language needs.

YOUR LANGUAGE NEEDS

1

A large part of this book will help you to identify and list **word partnerships** which are particularly useful for you. This page explains how and why learning word partnerships will help you.

Here is a simple, general example. If you think of football the first word which comes to mind is probably **ball**. If you think of more 'football words' you will probably choose **nouns** like **match, team**. Most people choose nouns. Often we start to think about a topic by starting with important nouns.

In business English you probably think first of words like **advert** or **sales.** But when we want to talk about something we need to know the **verbs** which often make a **word partnership** with the noun.

You can't talk about a game of football unless you know the words which are often used with **ball:**

head a ball	**kick the ball**	**pass the ball**
lob the ball	**throw the ball**	

From **one** useful noun, we can identify **a group** of useful verbs.

Another kind of word partnership in English is made by making a partnership of two nouns:

football match	**football supporter**	**football ground**
football season	**football league**	**football club**

You can see that from one word we can cover a very wide area by identifying **word partnerships**.

It is the same with the business words:

place an advert;	**appoint an advertising agency;**	
increase sales;	**a sales conference;**	**launch a sales campaign.**

Pages 57 to 76 will help you to create **your own personalised word partnership** lists.

From a few words, your teacher can help you to identify a lot of language you will find immediately useful to talk about your professional and personal interests.

Time spent identifying the language which is most useful for you is not wasted. The process of thinking about, and talking about your needs will help you to learn English efficiently.

INTRODUCTION

2

Every professional needs to talk about their work. But we are not usually happy talking to people if we know nothing about them. In different countries people talk more or less about themselves, their families and their interests when they are meeting people professionally. But everyone needs to be able to say something about themselves. The next few pages will help you to say something about yourself in English. You can complete the pages you think will be useful for you. If you are not happy to answer the questions – don't answer them. You do not need to say anything you are not happy to say.

These pages are to help you to say what you want to say. Please use them in that way.

On page 150 you will find ideas to help you think about the topics which you think professional people can talk about with contacts that they do not know very well. Remember, these are often different in different parts of the world, but finally, what you want to talk about is for you to decide!

In addition to talking about your professional life, you can help a teacher to help you find the personal language you need by using some of these things:

A CV /Resumé

Photographs

A map/guide of your home town/region

YOURSELF

2

Complete the following sentences about yourself.

I was born in _____ (place)

              in _____ (when)

I went to school   in _____ (place)

                        at _____ (type)

My parents came from _____

After leaving school, I studied _____ (subject)

                                    at _____

I did | a degree | **in** _____ (subject)
         | a course |
         | an apprenticeship |

After that I _____

My first job was in _____

                as a(n) _____

More recently I have been working as _____ (job)

                                    in _____ (where)

                                  with _____ (company)

After you have completed this page, check that you remember all the important language by covering one column and recalling the complete sentences. Notice the prepositions. Can you make questions to ask someone else about him- or herself?

As every business person knows, you don't talk about business all the time. Talking about yourself and your business partner can help to build trust and confidence. But different countries talk about different topics and have different taboo topics. Prepare yourself by thinking about your own attitudes (see pages 147 to 159) and the language you need.

YOUR JOB

2

Complete the following sentences about yourself.

My address is _____

My business number is _____

My extension is _____

I work for _____ (company)

        as a(n) _____ (job)

        in the _____ (department)

I mostly deal with _____ (kind of work)

I am responsible   for _____ (...ing form)

        and _____

My job involves a lot of _____ (...ing form)

        and _____

What I like about my job is _____

I've been with the company for _____ (period of time)

        since _____ (point in time)

I've been in my present job for _____

After you have completed the page, check that you remember from time to time by covering one column and recalling the whole sentence. Can you make questions to ask someone else for the same information?

YOUR COMPANY 1

2

Draw an organigram of your company. It should show the main structure of the organisation. Label the different parts of the organisation and the jobs in the organisation. As well as some of the words below, you may need special words used in your company.

division   department   section   unit
marketing   sales   production   finance   R and D   production   personnel
chairman   president   vice-chairman   board of directors   managing director
chief executive   director   manager
assistant   deputy   temporary

YOUR COMPANY 2

Complete the right-hand part of this page. Make complete sentences about your company. From time to time, cover one half of the page and recall the complete sentences.

The company is divided into

We employ

Our main branches are in

We have subsidiaries in

The company was founded in

I am mostly concerned with

I am responsible to
               for

Our parent company is

Apart from ourselves, they are also extensively involved in

The people I am in most frequent contact with are (jobs, not names)

Remember to check that you can say both halves of the sentence naturally — both the information about your own company, and the correct grammar for the first half of each sentence.

YOUR COMPANY 3

2

Complete this table with real information. Make sure you can use all the words in the table to talk about your situation.

Our	main major most important	product(s) services(s) customers clients competitors (export) market(s) domestic suppliers foreign suppliers priorities targets current projects problems	used to be is / are has / have been will be	_____ _____ _____ _____ _____

Write the initials of four people who are important in your work situation. They can be colleagues, clients, contacts in other companies etc. Then write their job, and some of the reasons why you have regular contact with them.

Initials	Job
Reasons	

Initials	Job
Reasons	

Initials	Job
Reasons	

Initials	Job
Reasons	

The language on this and the previous two pages provides a skeleton for talking about a lot of different parts of your daily life.

YOUR PRODUCT

2

Most companies offer a product or service. Write the name in English of three or four of the most important products/services which your organisation makes/offers.

_____

_____

Write here key words you need to **describe** the products/services. Try to choose words which describe the product in different ways: **size, shape, use.**

_____

_____

_____

_____

Very often in business you want to **compare** a product to an earlier product or a product made by a competitor. Write words here which will help you to compare the products/services you have listed above.

_____

_____

You will also want to talk about **advantages** and **disadvantages** of different products. Choose words to help you to do that and list them here.

_____

_____

_____

You may need a dictionary to help you to find the important words on this page. You will find many of the words you have on this page will help you to choose key words for **word families** (Page 96) and **keywords** (Page 58). You need also to check which verbs will be most help to you (Page 138).

YOUR VALUES

2

Language is for talking about more than business and facts. It can also help you to show what you think, believe and value.

Complete the following honestly.

What is most important to you?

	healthy	_____
	successful	_____
TO BE	correct	_____
	happy	_____
	useful	_____
	_____	_____

	time	fun
	money	friends
TO HAVE	security	_____
	status	_____
	comfort	_____
	_____	_____

	well	_____
TO DO	with other people	_____
THINGS	your way	_____
	at your own speed	_____
	efficiently	_____
	_____	_____

Later add more expressions which can be used to make sentences with

TO BE, TO HAVE, and TO DO.

From time to time select three items and remind yourself:

It is important to me to be _____ , to have _____ and to do

things _____ because _____

YOUR PHILOSOPHY

Complete each of these sentences. Don't just fill in the spaces quickly. Think about what you might want to say in English one day. Use the page to help you to use language which is really important to you.

Two of my favourite expressions are....

I think I am....

Other people say I am....

For me, success is....

My work is important to me because....

Money is....

For me, knowing English is....

For me, pleasure is....

For me, learning new things is....

The most important thing about my country for me is....

YOUR FAMILY AND FRIENDS

2

Write down here the initials of **five** people you know well. They can be members of your family, friends, colleagues, clients.

☐ ☐ ☐ ☐ ☐

Business people don't talk business all the time. Sometimes we talk about ourselves and people we know. If necessary use a dictionary to make sure you know all these words which are used to describe people.

amusing	aggressive	kind	talented	shy
ambitious	serious	calm	cheerful	fussy
stubborn	hard-working	dynamic	talkative	methodical
lively	strong	decisive	indecisive	considerate
untidy	sociable	loyal	moody	enterprising
easy-going	successful	cold	warm	rigid
optimistic	pessimistic	realistic	idealistic	impulsive
bossy	conscientious	quiet	sensitive	emotional
sincere	honest	out-spoken	reliable	hard
astute	bright	single-minded	careless	relaxed

Put the initials of the people you have chosen beside **three** words for each person. Choose words which describe that person.

Underline all the words which you think are positive in one colour. Use a different colour to underline the words you think are negative.

Use the initials of the people you have listed to start some of these sentences. They give you another way of talking about what people are like. Complete the sentences (silently!) with true information.

☐
doesn't find it easy to ....
is (not) very good at ....ing
has difficulty in ....ing
is (not) very interested in ....
spends a lot of time ....ing

☐
never misses a chance to ....
has the habit of ....ing
believes strongly in ....
is (not) very enthusiastic about ......
has no idea how to ....

Y ou will find it easier to remember any new words or expressions if you fix them in your mind by thinking about people you know and associating the words with the people and with qualities that you like and dislike.

INTRODUCTION

There is some language everyone needs, and which is difficult to learn in class. It is the language we use in social situations, when we want to be polite and pleasant to other people.

Social language uses a lot of fixed expressions. Often you can't translate from your own language – you need to learn natural English expressions. This section will help you with all these important areas:

Essential words
Apologies
Saying 'No'
Saying 'Yes'
Active listening
Language problems
'Would'
Eating out
Visitors
Word lobsters

The last pages of the section, which we call word lobsters, give you a special shape to record your own sentences which start with expressions which are very common in social situations. They are introduced on page 41.

ESSENTIAL WORDS

SAYING THANK YOU

Thank you.

Thank you very much.

Use these if someone does something simple for you. This is for things you normally expect from other people. They are not strong enough for special help.

Thanks a lot. (informal)

I'm very grateful.

It's very kind of you.

For special help, add one of these to the usual expressions listed above.

REQUESTS AND INVITATIONS

Could you......, please.

Would you...for me, please.

Use 'please' at the end of requests for help when the other person will do something for you.
Avoid using 'please' in the middle of a sentence.

A black coffee, please.

Please sit down.

Please help yourselves to the coffee.

Use 'please' as the beginning of invitations or suggestions where the other person will do something for themself.

Please don't wait for me.

Please join us this evening.

WHEN YOU ARE LISTENING

Sorry?

Use this word alone if you want the other person to repeat what they said for any reason – you didn't hear properly, you didn't understand, or even, you didn't believe what you heard!

Really?

Use this alone to ask the other person to continue, to give more details. It shows you are involved in the conversation but expect the other person to say more before you comment yourself.

If your English is not very good, these words will help you to take a natural part in a conversation without you having to say very much! If your English is good, it is important to use these words naturally.

APOLOGIES

I'M AFRAID

Match the remarks, and responses. Write your answers in the table below.

3

1. **Can you ring me this evening.**

   a. **Not completely, I'm afraid.**

2. **Could I speak to...please?**

   b. **I'm afraid that's impossible.**

3. **Did you remember to send me that fax?**

   c. **I'm afraid I completely forgot.**

4. **I'd need about 40% discount.**

   d. **I'm afraid I can't.**

5. **Are you happy with that suggestion?**

   e. **I'm afraid he's out at the moment.**

6. **What about next Tuesday?**

   f. **I'm afraid I can't manage next week at all.**

1	2	3	4	5	6

Add **'I'm afraid'** to any response which will seem unhelpful to the other person. Notice, it makes some quite strong negative responses acceptable.

It is not usually used in written English; in writing, use **'unfortunately'** instead.

Often, instead of the single word 'No', it is better to use **'I'm afraid not'** as a negative response.

OTHER APOLOGIES

In British English the easiest general rule is:

Excuse me	**before** you disturb someone. **before** you try to pass someone.
Sorry!	**after** you have inconvenienced someone.
Excuse me	is only used **after** you have done something in British English after you have coughed, sneezed, etc.

In American English, **'Excuse me'** is used to apologise **after** you have inconvenienced someone else.

SAYING 'NO'

It is very important to avoid using 'No' on its own unless you are annoyed. On its own it usually sounds aggressive and unhelpful. There are many other ways of giving a negative response. Match these remarks and responses.

1. Did your Head Office agree?   **a. No, not yet.**

2. Coffee?   **b. I'm afraid I've no idea.**

3. What's the code for Birmingham?   **c. I'd rather you didn't.**

4. Have they confirmed the order yet?   **d. Not at the moment, thank you.**

5. Do you mind if I arrive a bit late?   **e. I'm afraid not.**

6. Is 25% all right?   **f. Well, I really need a bit more than that.**

Collect more ways of saying 'No' naturally. Check by covering the English and recalling the natural English expressions.

1	2	3	4	5	6

YOUR LANGUAGE | ENGLISH

SAYING 'NO'

List expressions used to answer 'No' naturally and pleasantly.

Make sure you know their equivalents in your own language. Check the English from time to time by covering the right hand column.

3

YOUR LANGUAGE	ENGLISH

SAYING 'YES'

There are lots of expressions which are more natural and polite than using the single word 'Yes'. Match these remarks and responses. Notice that the natural expressions are quite different from simple, one-word answers.

3

1. **Will delivery by the end of the month be all right?**

2. **Could I have another cup of coffee?**

3. **Is it OK to park here?**

4. **Would you like me to copy it for you?**

5. **Can I count on your support?**

6. **Is next Thursday suitable for our next meeting?**

a. **Yes, I think so.**

b. **Yes, please.**

c. **Of course; help yourself.**

d. **Yes, that'll be fine.**

e. **As far as I'm concerned.**

f. **Yes. I'm in complete agreement.**

Write your answers here:

1	2	3	4	5	6

Collect more ways of saying 'Yes' and list them below. Check that you know the natural expressions by covering the English and recalling them.

YOUR LANGUAGE	ENGLISH

SAYING 'YES'

In English you do not usually reply with the single word 'Yes'. One-word replies can sound aggressive or rude. It is natural to answer with a short phrase or sentence.

During your course, listen for these replies. Note them here. Make a list of similar phrases in your own language. Check you have learned the natural English by covering the English and trying to recall the natural language.

3

YOUR LANGUAGE	ENGLISH

ACTIVE LISTENING

3

Different countries have different customs (see page 147) but in many places people who are speaking expect their listener to show interest and involvement. If you listen in complete silence, people may think you are difficult to talk to! Make a list of sounds or expressions which you can use to show you are listening.

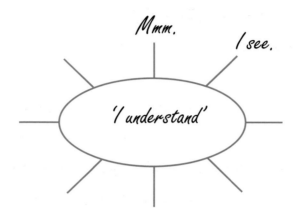

Mmm.

I see.

'I understand'

Make a list of expressions you can use to show you do not understand, or need something repeated or explained.

I don't quite follow.

_____

Sorry. What exactly do you mean?

_____

_____

_____

_____

_____

_____

LANGUAGE PROBLEMS

If you find it difficult to understand natural English conversation you need expressions to help you to control what other people say. Make sure you know how to use all the expressions below.

3

WHEN YOU DON'T UNDERSTAND

Sorry, I'm afraid I don't understand. (at all)

I don't know what......**means.** (You really don't know.)

I don't know what you mean by...... (You think you must misunderstand)

Just a moment, please. What (exactly) does........**mean?** (To check)

I didn't catch/follow that (completely). Could you just go over it again?

Could you just repeat that, please? (You want everything repeated.)

Could you just repeat (the figures/the dates/your fax number/...) **please?**

SAYING WHAT YOU NEED

Could I just have a minute, please. (You want a pause to think/write/....)

Could you just say that slowly, so I can make a note, please.

Could you spell (your name/address/company name/....), **please.**

EXPLAINING YOUR LANGUAGE PROBLEMS

I'm afraid I don't know the English word for...... . **Can you help me?**

I'm afraid I can't explain very clearly in English. (But I'll do my best.)

Have I made myself clear? (Gives the other person chance to check with you.)

I think you must have misunderstood me. (The other person seems annoyed or confused.)

YOU NEED TIME TO REACT

Really? (See page 28)

Can you give a few more details (about.......), **please?**

That's very interesting. It really gives me something to think about.

WOULD 1

REQUESTS

Would you	take a copy of this for me, please. ask him to phone please. let me know as soon as possible, please.

OFFERS

Would you like us to	fax it for you? book a hotel for you? call a taxi for you?

Would you like to	join us for dinner? phone your office before we start?

Would you like	some coffee? a copy?

SUGGESTIONS

If I were you, I'd.....(sell now).

PREFERENCES

Wouldn't it be better to	meet as soon as possible. come back to this question later?

I'd prefer	a soft drink, if you don't mind. to go by train.

INTRODUCING A COMMENT

I'd like to	begin by .... agree, but .... welcome you to .... ask if .... add that .... move on to ....

WOULD 2

WOULD

There are many useful expressions which begin with different phrases that all include **would** or **'d**. List the ones which are most useful for you here.

3

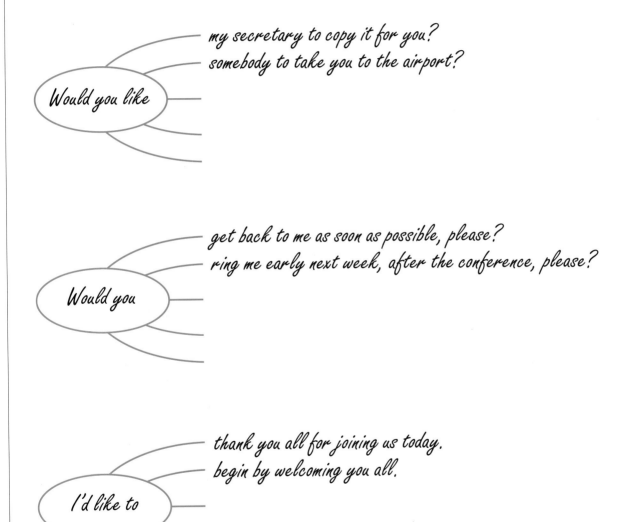

Would you like — my secretary to copy it for you?
— somebody to take you to the airport?

Would you — get back to me as soon as possible, please?
— ring me early next week, after the conference, please?

I'd like to — thank you all for joining us today.
— begin by welcoming you all.

Remember, if you say the expressions aloud several times, and then say them onto a cassette tape which you listen to later, it will help you to remember and feel comfortable with the new language.

EATING OUT 1

3

Every professional person knows how important it is to be able to meet colleagues and clients over food or a drink as well as in the office or at meetings. Sometimes this social language is difficult. Here are the most important words and expressions to help you.

Here are some important words you can use as word partnerships with the word **restaurant.** Make sure you know the equivalent in your language

a popular restaurant	**a first class restaurant**
a Chinese restaurant	**a simple Italian restaurant**
a famous Greek restaurant	**an excellent French restaurant**
an interesting seafood restaurant	**a nearby Indian restaurant**

MAKING ARRANGEMENTS

I thought we might go to a........restaurant I know, this evening.

I've booked a table for (eight o'clock) at a........restaurant.

Shall I pick you up at your hotel about (quarter to eight)?

I'll ask........to pick you up about (half past seven).

BEFORE THE MEAL

Would you like a drink to begin with (or shall we order straightaway)?

Can I suggest the............ . It's a local speciality.

They serve very good...........if you like it/them.

CHOOSING

I think I'll have the..........please.

The same for me, please.

DURING THE MEAL

This is very good. How's your........?

Would you like a little more.....?

Oh, thank you./No thanks. I'm fine.

LEAVING

Can we have the bill please.

Do you take VISA/American Express, please.

Could you call us a taxi, please.

EATING OUT 2

Make a list of three or four things to eat or drink which are local specialities which you might suggest a visitor could try. Can you explain them in English? Don't translate, explain. These expressions might help you:

It's/They're a sort of ....

It's/They're a bit like ....

It's got ....**in it.**

It's/They're cooked with ....

Be careful! It's very spicy/strong.

Put your list on the left, and write a full explanation on the right. Check later by covering the explanation to see if you can remember it.

LOCAL SPECIALITY	EXPLANATION IN ENGLISH

VISITORS

The language of the short speeches when we greet visitors or thank people at the end of a visit is very standardised. You can use these on most occasions.

GREETING VISITORS

❝ **Good morning (Ladies and Gentlemen). On behalf of........may I welcome you to........ . It is a great pleasure to have you with us today. I hope you enjoy your visit/meeting/the conference. If there is anything we can do to help, please do not hesitate to ask. Now, you don't want to listen to me all day so I'll hand you over to my colleague ....(who will show you...../take you to......).** ❞

A TOAST WITH VISITORS

❝ **Ladies and Gentlemen, could I just say a few words. It is a great pleasure to have you with us today. We hope you have enjoyed your visit. We are delighted to have had the opportunity to show you......../introduce ....to you/ meet so many of you (personally). We look forward to getting to know you all better/building on our already very successful co-operation/providing you with the service you need. So, let's raise our glasses to our future co-operation.** ❞

THANKING FOR A VISIT

❝ **Could I just say a few words? On behalf of........and myself may I express our warmest thanks for today's visit/the last few days/........ . I'm sure I speak for everyone when I say we have found the visit/meeting/........ very interesting and useful. We are very grateful to everyone who has helped to make our visit/ the meeting so rewarding and enjoyable. (I should particularly like to thank........ who was responsible fo the arrangements.) Thank you very much. We hope we may soon/one day/........ have the pleasure of welcoming (some of) you to............. .** ❞

WORD LOBSTER 1

The first words of some sentences are very common and very important in the language needed by business people. Some of the most important are listed for you. There is also space for you to add your own important examples.

It is very difficult to remember language which is just lists of new words. These special shapes, which we call 'word lobsters' will help you to remember more easily. Fill the 'legs' with useful expressions. Add a translation if you think it helps you. From time to time, cover the right hand part of the page and make sure you can recall the important expressions you have listed.

3

have a short break, shall we?
come back to that point later.

Let's

we meet again on the 17th?
you ring me again early next week?

May I suggest

Try to write natural sentences about your own business. These will be more useful and easier to remember.

WORD LOBSTER 2

Fill the important first words of other sentences that you may need to help you to have a natural conversation. Complete the legs of the lobster in the same way as on the previous page. Cover the expressions from time to time to check what you have learned.

3

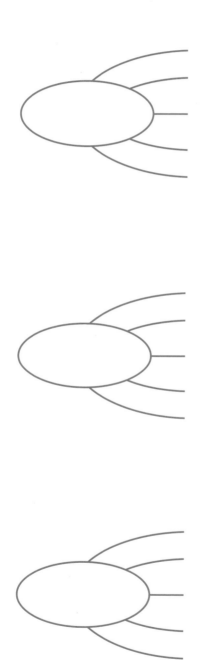

WORD LOBSTER 3

Fill the important first words of other sentences that you may need to help you to have a natural conversation. Complete the legs of the lobster in the same way as on the previous page. Cover the expressions from time to time to check what you have learned.

3

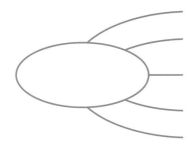

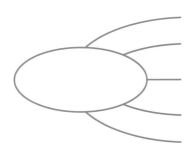

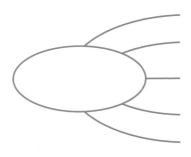

WORD LOBSTER 4

Fill the important first words of other sentences that you may need to help you to have a natural conversation. Complete the legs of the lobster in the same way as on the previous page. Cover the expressions from time to time to check what you have learned.

3

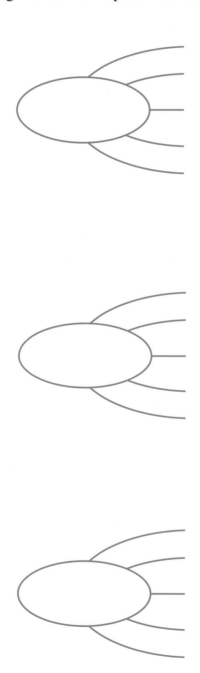

USING PROFESSIONAL TEXTS

One of the most important parts of your professional language course is the part you make yourself with your teacher. You need to select language useful to you from natural professional texts.

Usually you read for information or pleasure. Here you are going to use texts for a completely different purpose — to help you find language you need. You will waste a lot of time if you try to understand every word.

This section of the book will help you to use texts to help your English.

In addition to reading you can also **listen** to natural English regularly. The BBC World Service has many helpful programmes, including the news and programmes of special interest to business people. You can use them in a similar way — as a resource to find language useful to you.

You will find it particularly useful to identify and record word partnerships around certain key words (see pages 57 to 76). Here are some sources of useful professional language texts:

Company brochures	Promotional materials
Product descriptions	Technical manuals
Product samples	Trade journals
In-house newsletters	Adverts
Examples of letters	Taped phone calls
Minutes of meetings	Company reports

You can also use newspapers to find topical business language. Two which are usually easy to get are:

The Financial Times	International Herald Tribune

4

USING HEADLINES 1

Use a newspaper such as the Financial Times. Look through the paper's headlines and other large print. Look for useful two-word partnerships. List the partnerships you find in a two column format. It will help you if you use different lists for different kinds of partnership, for example adjective-noun. Here are some from one issue of a newspaper:

hostile reaction

prime rates

slower sales

political and economic pressures

Green Consumers

Brutal repression

Best Value

List them like this:

ADJECTIVE	NOUN	ADJECTIVE	NOUN
hostile	reaction	prime	rates
brutal	repression	green	consumers
slower	sales	political	pressure(s)
	value	economic	pressure(s)

After you have made the lists, check regularly if you can remember by covering one column and recalling the words in the other column.

It will help you to remember the partnerships if you think of a strong image or picture for each one. It also helps if you try to identify some personal meaning for each partnership you record. Take time while you are choosing and recording them. It is an investment of time. You will have the profit when you remember better.

USING HEADLINES 2

Here are some more large print examples from the paper. What kind of words are used to make these word partnerships? These are two more kinds of partnership which you can list in two columns on the following pages. Put headings on the columns below.

outlines the problems

makes the initial decisions

launch campaign

relieve stress

take a year off

halt negotiations

....	....
outline	a/the problem
make	a decision

....	....
launch	a campaign
take	a year off

opinion poll

election victory

power struggle

Book Trade

Sales Personnel

CAREER OPPORTUNITIES

....	....
opinion	poll
book	trade

....	....
power	struggle
career	opportunities

USING AN ARTICLE 1

4

Take an article and search through for word partnerships. Remember, you need to choose the article and choose the word partnerships. Most people do not need partnerships like *optical bleaches,* but many more people will use *environmentally friendly, ordinary people, a small percentage.* **Choose the partnerships you think will be useful to you.**

As an example only, how many useful word partnerships can you find in this article? Underline them as you read the article.

Providing environment-friendly goods has great marketing potential as shoppers start to put ecological soundness first

The biggest market opportunities are in the fast-moving consumer-goods area – washing powder, household cleaning supplies, paper products and food – because these are the sort of products that ordinary people have to buy every day.

Last month's launch of a new range of ecologically friendly cleaning products, under the Ark brand name, guided by Bryn Jones, a former Greenpeace director, is a good example of the greening of our supermarket shelves.

What is special about Ark products is that they do not contain phosphates, which can get into rivers and kill fish and plants, nor chlorine bleach, which can produce dioxin, a carcinogenic compound, nor biological enzymes, which have been linked with skin problems.

Will Ark products actually be accepted by the customer as doing the job as well as conventional, non-ecologically sound cleaners? Take whiteness, for example: most washing powders contain so-called optical bleaches, which make clothes look whiter than white.

That is, of course, the crux of the matter: only a small percentage of the public will put ecological soundness above all other considerations when filling a supermarket trolley. Most consumers will put other priorities, such as whiteness, above green-ness.

Yet the indications are that the green consumer movement is growing in strength, especially among mothers with young children – and, let's face it, it is still women who do most of the shopping.

So what kind of products are likely to appeal to the green consumers? Ark has demonstrated that there is a demand for green cleaners, and the success of the Body Shop is clear proof that there is a ready market for green cosmetics.

Parents' concerns over chlorine bleaches used in disposable nappies and other paper products has led to the greening of the nappy. Increasingly, battery manufacturers are describing their products as environmentally friendly. Lead-free petrol is becoming more popular.

The recent concern over contamination of foodstuffs has fuelled an already growing movement towards cleaner, healthier food in our shops.

Anyone who has paused by the organic-food displays in leading supermarkets cannot but be struck by two immediate facts: people are prepared to pay well over the odds for food they believe to be less contaminated with "artificial" fertilizers and pesticides, and, for some reason, the more "organic" the produce is, the more earth seems to be sticking to it.

But reseach shows that the public is not fooled by a label saying "green" on a product, or by a few cosmetic changes – and Britain's major manufacturers have recognized this.

There is a list on the opposite page.

USING AN ARTICLE 2

Here are some of the partnerships you may have found in the article opposite. You can list them in the usual two-column format, or, if you find three-word partnerships, you can list these by using a mark like this (▼)

great ▼		ecologically	friendly
marketing	potential	brand	name
fast-moving	consumer-goods	a small	percentage
washing	powder	put above ▼	
household ▼		other	considerations
cleaning	supplies	appeal to ▼	
ordinary	people	the green	consumer

By listing the word partnerships in this way you can check what you can remember very easily. Can you recall the missing words in these partnerships? — if not, check in the article.

	shelves		petrol
clear		fuelled	
	market		
parents'		pay well	

When you think you have learned some useful combinations, write a short summary of the article (or part of it). Use as many of the partnerships as you can, but without looking at the article or list while you are writing.

Choosing articles which contain word partnerships useful to talk about your business and interests is a very efficient way of improving your English.

VERB - NOUN PARTNERSHIPS

Choose your own texts. Use them in the same way as the text on page 48.
List useful partnerships from the texts you choose here.

4

VERB	NOUN	VERB	NOUN

ADJECTIVE - NOUN PARTNERSHIPS

Choose your own texts. Use them in the same way as the text on page 48.
List useful partnerships from the texts you choose here.

ADJECTIVE	NOUN	ADJECTIVE	NOUN

4

NOUN - NOUN PARTNERSHIPS

Choose your own texts. Use them in the same way as the text on page 48.
List useful partnerships from the texts you choose here.

4

NOUN	NOUN

NOUN	NOUN

USEFUL EXPRESSIONS 1

While you are using texts to find and list useful word partnerships, you will certainly find some useful expressions and idioms as well. It is not as easy to list these in a system, but again we suggest you write them so you can cover part of the expression, or write an equivalent in your own language which you can cover later when you want to check what you have learned. Use the following pages to record useful language. Here are a few expressions to suggest the kind of language you and your teacher can look for together.

4

ENGLISH	YOUR LANGUAGE
worth a look	
across the country	
absolutely free	
hopes and fears	
we are committed to excellence	

USEFUL EXPRESSIONS 2

Use this page to record useful expressions and idioms. Give equivalents in your own language. Check by covering your language, or by covering part of the English expression.

4

ENGLISH   YOUR LANGUAGE

_____   _____

_____   _____

_____   _____

_____   _____

_____   _____

_____   _____

_____   _____

_____   _____

_____   _____

_____   _____

_____   _____

_____   _____

_____   _____

_____   _____

USEFUL EXPRESSIONS 3

Use this page to record useful expressions and idioms. Give equivalents in your own language. Check by covering your language, or by covering part of the English expression.

ENGLISH

YOUR LANGUAGE

4

USEFUL EXPRESSIONS 2

Use this page to record useful expressions and idioms. Give equivalents in your own language. Check by covering your language, or by covering part of the English expression.

4

ENGLISH	YOUR LANGUAGE

KEYWORDS

Several sections of this book help you to identify and record words which often occur together. (The technical name for these is 'collocations'.) If you want to talk about your **car** you will certainly need the word partnerships **buy a new car, park the car, leave the car at home.** From a single **keyword** we can collect and organise the words which are the basic material for many natural sentences. This section

a. presents a group of important keywords for business English and helps you find and record important word partnerships.

b. gives you space to choose your own keywords and find and record their important word partnerships.

The keywords presented in this section are:

> **Contract/Agreement**
> **Sales** (These pages show you how to use the section)
> **Price(s)**
> **Costs**
> **Market**
> **Advertising**
> **Production**
> **Product**
> **Company**
> **Department/Office**
> **Order**
> **Offer**
> **Tax(es)**
> **Staff/Personnel**

This is followed by several pages for your own keywords.

5

KEYWORDS INTRODUCTION 1

Many professional words are regularly used with a small number of other words. Instead of learning individual words you will find it much more useful to learn word partnerships. In the middle of the diagram is a **keyword.** Around it are **background words** of two different kinds. Underline them with two different coloured pens.

5

alter   unworkable   discuss   conditional   temporary   modify

exclusive   sign   break   check   draft   draw up   outline

go over

A CONTRACT
AN AGREEMENT

negotiate   satisfactory

terminate   export   short-term

non-renewable   trade   sales   one-year

legal   renew   licensing   reject   review

In this example you should have:

    Verbs which go in front of the keyword: **sign** an agreement.
    Words which go **between** the verb and the keyword: sign a **temporary/trade** agreement.

Make a list of word partnerships. Find two-word partnerships
(verb + keyword) or three-word partnerships (verb + adjective/noun + keyword)

_____   _____   _____

_____   _____   _____

U sually on the following pages we then suggest that you write some sentences about your own situation using some of the partnerships. As usual, this will help you remember the partnerships better.

KEYWORDS INTRODUCTION 2

Not all the keywords work in the same way. Sometimes the keyword is at the centre of a word partnership. In the diagram below you need to find words which **follow** the keyword: sales **strategy**, sales **drive.** Underline these in one colour. Now underline verbs which can come **in front of one of the two-word partnerships** you have made: **discuss** sales strategy, **launch** a sales drive.

5

In these examples the three-word partnerships are often almost complete sentences: **We need to discuss our sales strategy**. Write some more three-word partnerships of this kind.

_____   _____   _____

_____   _____   _____

As usual we will ask you to write sentences about your own situation.

W ith these word partnerships you can often say a lot without using difficult grammar. Instead of *'How many of these can we sell in America?'* it is quicker, easier and more natural to say *'What's the American sales potential ?'*

KEYWORDS 1

The word in the centre of the diagram is the **keyword**. There are different kinds of words in the **background** words. Use different coloured pens to underline the background words so that you divide them into groups. Find some two-word and three-word partnerships. Look for some partnerships which include **the keyword** and **a verb** from the background words. Write four sentences about your own situation. Use coloured pens or highlight the word partnerships so you can check them easily later.

alter   unworkable   discuss   conditional   temporary   modify

sign   break   check   draft   draw up

exclusive   outline

go over

A CONTRACT

AN AGREEMENT   negotiate   satisfactory

terminate

export   short-term

non-renewable   one-year

legal   trade   sales

renew   licensing   reject   review

_____ _____ _____

_____ _____ _____

_____

_____

_____

_____

KEYWORDS 2

The word in the centre of the diagram is the **keyword**. There are different kinds of words in the **background** words. Use different coloured pens to underline the background words so that you divide them into groups. Find some two-word and three-word partnerships. Look for some partnerships which include **the keyword** and **a verb** from the background words. Write four sentences about your own situation. Use coloured pens or highlight the word partnerships so you can check them easily later.

area   representative   launch   present   volume

forecast   drive

target   increase   discuss   calculate

boost   maintain   pay   **SALES**   set   technique   prospect

figures   meeting

manager   potential   commission   call

assess   fix   reach   win/lose

adopt   report   quota   extend

strategy   call on

_____ _____ _____

_____ _____ _____

_____

_____

_____

_____

KEYWORDS 3

The word in the centre of the diagram is the **keyword**. There are different kinds of words in the **background** words. Use different coloured pens to underline the background words so that you divide them into groups. Find some two-word and three-word partnerships. Look for some partnerships which include **the keyword** and **a verb** from the background words. Write four sentences about your own situation. Use coloured pens or highlight the word partnerships so you can check them easily later.

5

offer

raise

fix

cash

cut

list

sale

reduce

range

quote

limit

lower

PRICE(S)

sensitivity

object to

reduction

retail

increase

discount

agree

rise

wholesale

_____ _____ _____

_____ _____ _____

_____

_____

_____

_____

KEYWORDS 4

The word in the centre of the diagram is the **keyword**. There are different kinds of words in the **background** words. Use different coloured pens to underline the background words so that you divide them into groups. Find some two-word and three-word partnerships. Look for some partnerships which include **the keyword** and **a verb** from the background words. Write four sentences about your own situation. Use coloured pens or highlight the word partnerships so you can check them easily later.

5

advertising   capital   analyse   unit
          cut   overhead
reduce   variable
          total
compare   *COSTS*   production

break down   material   labour
                                           bring down
absorb   fixed   indirect   increase
          spread   direct   average

_____   _____   _____

_____   _____   _____

_____

_____

_____

_____

KEYWORDS 5

The word in the centre of the diagram is the **keyword**. There are different kinds of words in the **background** words. Use different coloured pens to underline the background words so that you divide them into groups. Find some two-word and three-word partnerships. Look for some partnerships which include **the keyword** and **a verb** from the background words. Write four sentences about your own situation. Use coloured pens or highlight the word partnerships so you can check them easily later.

5

carry out   capture   survey

break into   response

enter   analyse   research

open   free   MARKET   seize

increase   buyer's

trends

move   leader   share   Japanese

European   sector

forces   growing   domestic

_____   _____   _____

_____   _____   _____

_____

_____

_____

_____

KEYWORDS 6

The word in the centre of the diagram is the **keyword**. There are different kinds of words in the **background** words. Use different coloured pens to underline the background words so that you divide them into groups. Find some two-word and three-word partnerships. Look for some partnerships which include **the keyword** and **a verb** from the background words. Write four sentences about your own situation. Use coloured pens or highlight the word partnerships so you can check them easily later.

conduct   campaign   agency

take   national   reduce

launch

prepare   TV   budget

ADVERTISING   slogan

style   rates

costs   press

space   regional   devise   trade

copy

concept   change   appoint

5

_____ _____ _____

_____ _____ _____

_____

_____

_____

_____

KEYWORDS 7

The word in the centre of the diagram is the **keyword**. There are different kinds of words in the **background** words. Use different coloured pens to underline the background words so that you divide them into groups. Find some two-word and three-word partnerships. Look for some partnerships which include **the keyword** and **a verb** from the background words. Write four sentences about your own situation. Use coloured pens or highlight the word partnerships so you can check them easily later.

5

capacity   control   start   train   line

set   system

license   site

        costs   efficient   hold up

halt

    transfer   PRODUCTION

                                                        engineer

problems   speed   plan

                                                        target

    levels   supervise   maintain   check

overcome   increase   automate

_____   _____   _____

_____   _____   _____

_____

_____

_____

_____

KEYWORDS 8

The word in the centre of the diagram is the **keyword**. There are different kinds of words in the **background** words. Use different coloured pens to underline the background words so that you divide them into groups. Find some two-word and three-word partnerships. Look for some partnerships which include **the keyword** and **a verb** from the background words. Write four sentences about your own situation. Use coloured pens or highlight the word partnerships so you can check them easily later.

sell

new   develop   range   specifications   advertise

promote

manager   modify   **(A/THE) PRODUCT**   design

features

distribute   promotion

test

demonstrate   improve   manufacture

launch   invent

5

These words can, of course, be used with the name of your particular product instead of the general word 'product'.

_____   _____   _____

_____   _____   _____

_____

_____

_____

KEYWORDS 9

The word in the centre of the diagram is the **keyword**. There are different kinds of words in the **background** words. Use different coloured pens to underline the background words so that you divide them into groups. Find some two-word and three-word partnerships. Look for some partnerships which include **the keyword** and **a verb** from the background words. Write four sentences about your own situation. Use coloured pens or highlight the word partnerships so you can check them easily later.

5

well-run   re-structure   invest in

buy into   found   car   register   run

join   oil   profitable   new

local   *A/THE*   big

holding   *COMPANY*

start up   take over   leave

        set up

foreign   float   finance   Public   Limited

subsidiary   work for   manage   medium-sized

_____   _____   _____

_____   _____   _____

_____

_____

_____

_____

KEYWORDS 10

The word in the centre of the diagram is the **keyword**. There are different kinds of words in the **background** words. Use different coloured pens to underline the background words so that you divide them into groups. Find some two-word and three-word partnerships. Look for some partnerships which include **the keyword** and **a verb** from the background words. Write four sentences about your own situation. Use coloured pens or highlight the word partnerships so you can check them easily later.

5

advertising

complaints

take over

run

supervise

marketing

be in charge of

sales

DEPARTMENT
OFFICE

(be) put in charge of

head

legal

finance

join

accounts

manage

re-structure

production

_____   _____   _____

_____   _____   _____

_____

_____

_____

_____

KEYWORDS 11

The word in the centre of the diagram is the **keyword**. There are different kinds of words in the **background** words. Use different coloured pens to underline the background words so that you divide them into groups. Find some two-word and three-word partnerships. Look for some partnerships which include **the keyword** and **a verb** from the background words. Write four sentences about your own situation. Use coloured pens or highlight the word partnerships so you can check them easily later.

5

phone about

initial

fax   lose   £3m

stock

confirm   regular

win   receive

repeat   place

(AN)
ORDER

dispatch   check

delay   wholesale

cancel   special   meet

get   initial

large   written

supply   bulk   handle

_____   _____   _____

_____   _____   _____

_____

_____

_____

_____

KEYWORDS 12

The word in the centre of the diagram is the **keyword**. There are different kinds of words in the **background** words. Use different coloured pens to underline the background words so that you divide them into groups. Find some two-word and three-word partnerships. Look for some partnerships which include **the keyword** and **a verb** from the background words. Write four sentences about your own situation. Use coloured pens or highlight the word partnerships so you can check them easily later.

detailed

submit   work

                                          revise

                provisional   revised

prepare

                    ⬭ (AN) OFFER ⬭   accept

        make   final

    receive   withdraw

            firm

5

_____   _____   _____

_____   _____   _____

_____

_____

_____

KEYWORDS 13

The word in the centre of the diagram is the **keyword**. There are different kinds of words in the **background** words. Use different coloured pens to underline the background words so that you divide them into groups. Find some two-word and three-word partnerships. Look for some partnerships which include **the keyword** and **a verb** from the background words. Write four sentences about your own situation. Use coloured pens or highlight the word partnerships so you can check them easily later.

5

levy

earnings   value added   capital

payer   close

pay   reduce   cuts

                                              liability   claim

                    TAX(ES)

be liable   income   allowance

                                      bracket

relief   deduct   lower   return   loophole

                avoid   inspector

year   code   consultant

                        complete

_____   _____   _____

_____   _____   _____

_____

_____

_____

KEYWORDS 14

The word in the centre of the diagram is the **keyword**. There are different kinds of words in the **background** words. Use different coloured pens to underline the background words so that you divide them into groups. Find some two-word and three-word partnerships. Look for some partnerships which include **the keyword** and **a verb** from the background words. Write four sentences about your own situation. Use coloured pens or highlight the word partnerships so you can check them easily later.

5

appoint   white-collar   employ   sales   lose

                                    hire   (un)skilled

recruit

        qualified   *STAFF*   need
trained   *PERSONNEL*   poach

        take on   key   office

well paid   look for
        motivate   train   interview

_____   _____   _____

_____   _____   _____

_____

_____

_____

_____

KEYWORDS 15

Now use your own keywords; collect background words by using a dictionary or talking to your teacher. Remember you need to be able to talk about yourself and your interests as well as your work!

KEYWORDS 16

Now use your own keywords; collect background words by using a dictionary or talking to your teacher. Remember you need to be able to talk about yourself and your interests as well as your work!

5

KEYWORDS 17

Now use your own keywords; collect background words by using a dictionary or talking to your teacher. Remember you need to be able to talk about yourself and your interests as well as your work!

INTRODUCTION

"Without grammar you can't say much, without vocabulary you can't say anything." Learning words is important, but learning grammar is important too.

Several sections of this book help you to identify and record the words, and the word partnerships, which will be particularly useful to you.

This section helps you to organise the parts of English grammar which are most important for business English. It helps you to say things accurately and naturally and to avoid mistakes. There are special pages to make a note of the language you need to avoid your own 'favourite' mistakes!

This is the largest section of the book and there are several separate sub-sections. These are:

6

General Business Grammar	The basic grammar to make a sentence more natural/diplomatic.
Being Diplomatic	Space to record important natural expressions.
Grammar of Change	How to talk about trends, graphs, increase/decrease etc.
Word Families	Keywords which have different forms and make important word partnerships. Space to make your own.
Business Verbs	Important verbs for talking about business conversations/discussions.
Have	Word partnerships with this key verb.
Two-word Verbs	These are a very important part of natural spoken English. Identify and record the most useful for you.
Business Prepositions	
Business Prefixes	
Important Mistakes	Space to record the correct English so you can avoid **your** mistakes.
Word Contrasts	More space to help you avoid mistakes.
Possibility and Neccessity	Ways to avoid unnatural English.
Your Work Situation	Verb forms needed to talk about yourself.

GENERAL BUSINESS GRAMMAR 1

There are some general remarks we can make about the language used to discuss and negotiate effectively in business. Usually we try to avoid sounding dogmatic or inflexible. Usually we hope to find a course of action which suits both parties. English grammar has special ways of doing this. The most general are given here. Notice them when you listen; use them when you present your own ideas. They will make your English more natural and more effective.

INTRODUCTORY PHRASES

Often we introduce our reaction with a word or phrase which tells the listener what kind of comment we are going to make. In particular some phrases warn the listener that disagreement follows. Here are the most common introductory phrases. Which ones are warnings?

Actually,	**With respect,**	**In those circumstances,**
Well,	**To be honest,**	**In fact,**
Frankly,	**As a matter of fact,**	**To put it bluntly,**

WOULD

Would is often added to make any statement more tentative. It takes away the dogmatic tone of many statements.

That is unacceptable.	**That would be unacceptable.**
That does not meet our requirements.	**That would not meet our requirements.**
We need further reassurance.	**We would need further reassurance.**

How could you make these more tentative?

1. That is too late.
2. I prefer to meet before that.
3. We expect them to accept our proposals.
4. We hope to be able to complete soon.
5. Flying has definite advantages.
6. I'm not able to give a guarantee at this stage.
7. Finance is no problem.
8. I'm afraid I don't accept that.

Write some examples of your own here:

_____

_____

_____

_____

GENERAL BUSINESS GRAMMAR 2

SUGGESTIONS

Often suggestions are presented in question form:

| That is too late. | ➔ | **Is that too late?** |
| That would be too late. | ➔ | **Would that be too late?** |

How could these be made more tentative?

30% is too much.
Friday would be convenient.
We need another meeting fairly soon.
We could ask the UN to finance the project.
It would be a good idea to involve the French.
We could cancel.
We've got to increase our offer.
They can raise some of the finance themselves.

The examples above all sound even more tentative and open to negotiation if they are grammatically negative:

Isn't that too late?
Wouldn't that be too late?

Can you change the other examples in the same way.

Write some examples useful in your job here:

_____

_____

_____

_____

_____

_____

_____

6

GENERAL BUSINESS GRAMMAR 3

QUALIFIERS

Successful meetings often depend on avoiding direct disagreement. The more general the statement, the more likely it is to produce disagreement. Not surprisingly, therefore, good negotiators often restrict general statements by using qualifiers. Here are some of the most common qualifiers English:

a **slight** misunderstanding	a **short** delay
a **little bit too** early	a **bit of a** problem
some reservations	a **little** more time

AVOIDING NEGATIVE WORDS

Often English avoids negative adjectives, preferring *not* + positive equivalent:

The hotel was dirty.	➔	**The hotel wasn't very clean.**
The food was cold.	➔	**The food was not very hot.**

Negative words used directly [*It was unacceptable*] are usually **very** negative.

COMPARATIVES

In offering an alternative suggestion, the comparative is often used:

Wouldn't the 31st be more convenient? It might be cheaper to go by air.

The implication is that the other person's suggestion is acceptable, but yours is **more** acceptable. For this reason the use of the comparative is more tactful.

This is not only true for adjectives. Notice these expressions. Each one contains an expression based on the comparative:

> **There's more chance of them accepting if we ....**
> **I still think they are more likely to agree if ....**
> **We need more information before we agree to anything.**

The language points discussed here are general features of English. The features in English may be very different from your own language. It is up to you to decide if you want to use all of the language points discussed here. It is essential, however, if you are going to use English in meetings with native speakers, that you are aware of the way they use English to make their message more direct, more tactful, more diplomatic etc.

BEING DIPLOMATIC 1

Use this page to record the natural way to say things diplomatically. Write and record your answers after you have checked with your teacher. Use the lower part of the page for your own examples, about your own job.

_____

(That's inconvenient. I don't want to meet so soon.)

_____

(We have had problems with our distributor.)

_____

(I can't accept such a long delay.)

_____

(That suggestion is useless!)

_____

(That's an unhelpful way of looking at the problem.)

_____

_____

_____

_____

_____

_____

6

BEING DIPLOMATIC 2

Use this page to record the natural way to say things diplomatically. Write and record your answers after you have checked with your teacher. Use the lower part of the page for your own examples, about your own job.

_____

(The last quarter's sales figures were bad.)

_____

(Next Tuesday is inconvenient.)

_____

(That's a negative attitude!)

_____

(I refuse to believe that!)

_____

(That leaves me with a problem!)

_____

_____

_____

_____

_____

_____

_____

_____

BEING DIPLOMATIC 3

Use this page to record the natural way to say things diplomatically. Write and record your answers after you have checked with your teacher. Use the lower part of the page for your own examples, about your own job.

_____

(They are a bad risk.)

_____

(It's a good idea to take a long-term view.)

_____

(It's dangerous to delay the decision too long.)

_____

(That's impossible!)

_____

(That's a stupid idea!)

_____

_____

_____

_____

_____

_____

Could you use very direct language in your language? Does the English seem strange? Do you think there could be problems in international discussions because languages are used differently in different countries? (See pages 150, 151, 159).

GRAMMAR OF CHANGE 1

IMPORTANT WORDS

Sentences like these are very common in business:

WORD PARTNERSHIP	'CHANGE' VERB	'HOW' WORD	WHEN, WHY ETC.
Oil prices	slumped	dramatically	last year.
Production costs	have risen	steadily	as a result of the budget.
Business confidence	will increase	sharply	if the dollar falls.

In business we often want to talk about changes or trends. It is easy to see that all the above sentences could be drawn as graphs. This section will help you with the language we use to put graphs into words.

The most important words are the 'change' verbs. Which of these are about an increase (↑), which about a decrease (↓) and which about staying the same (→)?

Mark the verb with the correct symbol.

rise	go up	peak
grow	increase	jump
come down	level off	decrease
fall	slump	decline
rocket	bottom out	improve
shrink	remain steady	hold firm

You can talk more effectively about changes if you also use a word to describe how the change happened:

slightly	_____	**sharply**	_____
suddenly	_____	**steadily**	_____
dramatically	_____	**gradually**	_____
slowly	_____	**immediately**	_____

Make sure you can use all these words. Check with a dictionary if necessary. Make sure you know the differences between the 'how' words. Write equivalents in your own language if you think it will help.

GRAMMAR OF CHANGE 2

SENTENCE PATTERN

Here are some basic 'change' words. Complete the other diagrams.

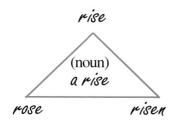
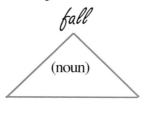
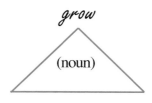

Think of a sentence to describe this graph. Write it down.

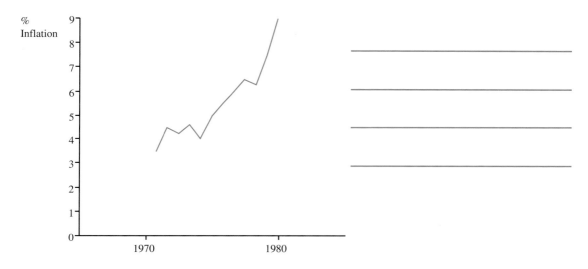

Compare your sentence with these:

Between 1970 and 1980 inflation rose **from** 4% **to** 9% (rose **by** 5%)
Inflation rose **by** 5% **between** 1970 and 1980. is an alternative
Notice the word order

        Time — Subject — Trend
or, sometimes   **Subject — Trend — Time**

Notice these two pattern sentences. Look particularly at the prepositions and the order of the different parts of the sentence.

Sales rose steadily by 200 units from 100 to 300 in the first quarter.

There was a steady rise in sales of 200 units in the first quarter.

The following pages will help you to use the language we need to talk about graphs accurately.

GRAMMAR OF CHANGE 3

VERB FORMS 1

Different forms of the verb have different meanings. Each one has certain time expressions that often occur with it. Here are some of the most useful. There is a short explanation of the verb form and some typical time expressions. All the sentences are ways of talking about the information which is given in the graphs.

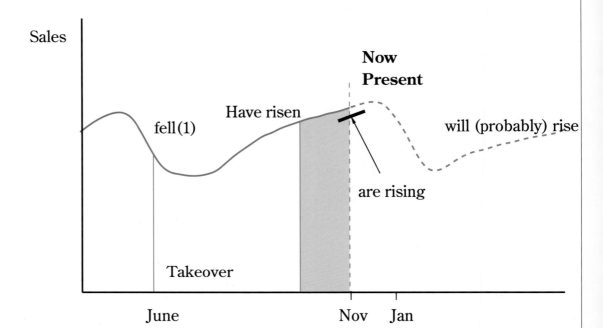

Sales *had fallen* before the take-over last year.
Sales *had been falling* before the take-over last year.

These verb forms **look back** on something in the past **from an important point in the past.**

Sales *have risen* in the last few months.(1)
Sales *have risen* since the take-over in June.(2)
Sales *have been rising* so we are quite pleased.(3)

This verb form **looks back from the present.** Sometimes you just look back (3); sometimes you give the **period** you are looking back over (1); and sometimes you give the **point** that you look back to (2), when the change began.

Sales *fell* in the summer.
Sales *fell* sharply before the take-over.

This verb form talks about something in the past, not connected to the present. Sentences like this **always have a time expression** to say exactly when in the past.

GRAMMAR OF CHANGE 4

VERB FORMS 2

Sales *are rising*.

This verb form always refers to the situation **around the present.** It describes a situation which started before the present and one the speaker thinks will continue for at least some time into the future.

———————————

Sales *will probably fall* in the New Year.
Sales *will almost certainly* level off next year.

This verb form refers to the future. It is not used for something in the future which is **absolutely** certain, so it is often used with words which say **how** certain the speaker is. Common ones are **probably, possibly, almost certainly, definitely.** The last means "as certain as we can be about the future".

———————————

Sales *rise* in the summer and *fall* in the autumn.

This form is used to talk about what is **usually** or **generally** true. It is not used for a trend, but for **a (regular) pattern.** There is no example of this on the graphs opposite, but it can describe, for example, the regular annual pattern found in many businesses.

TALKING ABOUT THE PRESENT SITUATION

Most often in business we want to talk about the situation now. This means two verb forms are particularly important:

AROUND NOW

Labour costs **are increasing** and our export customers are starting to complain. (The present continuous)

UP TO NOW

Our prices **have increased** recently and our customers have started to complain. (The present perfect)

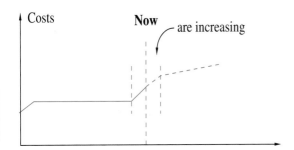

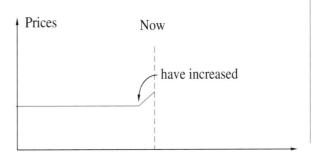

GRAMMAR OF CHANGE 5

PREPOSITIONS 1

List the time expressions which can be used with these prepositions. Notice the verb forms which are used frequently with the expressions you record. All these prepositions are often used with 'change' verbs.

6

SINCE +point

Prices have risen...

since the middle of 1990

FOR +period

Prices have fallen.....
Prices fell.....
Prices will rise....

for longer than we expected

OVER +period

Prices have risen....
Prices rose....
Prices will rise......

over the last/next few months

DURING +period

Prices rose....
Prices have risen......
Prices are rising......
Prices will rise......

during the pre-election period

GRAMMAR OF CHANGE 6

PREPOSITIONS 2

List the time expressions which can be used with these prepositions. Notice the verb forms which are used frequently with the expressions you record. All these prepositions are often used with 'change' verbs.

6

BY + point

Prices rose......
Prices had risen......
Prices will have risen....

by the end of the (financial) year

AT + point

Prices rose.....
Prices will rise.....

at the beginning/end of (July)

IN +period

Prices rose....
Prices have risen......
Prices will rise......

in the first/last three months of the year

ON +period

Prices rose....
Prices will rise......

on the first of January

GRAMMAR OF CHANGE 7

EXPRESSIONS OF TIME

Here is a list of expressions of time. It includes many useful ones, but you can add many more.

The most important difference is between **periods** and expressions which are used as **points** in time. Some of the expressions in this list can be used as both:

> We reduced our staff by 12% **during last year.** (period)
> We have reduced our staff by 12% **since last year.** (point)

Use the two columns to sort the expressions we have given and then add more of your own.

1992
October
the afternoon
two o'clock
the summer
the beginning / end of
last / next weekend / month / year
the last / next quarter / few months / half-year

PERIODS

_____ _____
_____ _____
_____ _____
_____ _____
_____ _____
_____ _____
_____ _____
_____ _____

POINTS

_____ _____
_____ _____
_____ _____
_____ _____
_____ _____
_____ _____
_____ _____
_____ _____

GRAMMAR OF CHANGE 8

PREPOSITIONAL PHRASES

In addition to the usual English prepositions (**in, on, at,** etc.) there are a number of preposition phrases made of more than one word. Some of these are important in professional English. Make sure you know the equivalent of each of these in your own language.

ENGLISH	YOUR LANGUAGE	ENGLISH	YOUR LANGUAGE
as a result of . . .		apart from . . .	
because of . . .		due to . . .	
except for . . .		in line with . . .	
in spite of . . .		in the face of . . .	
in view of . . .		on top of . . .	
regardless of . . .		with reference to . . .	

Use some of the expressions above to write about trends in your own situation. Choose 'change' verbs and prepositions from the previous pages.

6

GRAMMAR OF CHANGE 9

SPECIAL EXPRESSIONS 1

Read this article about inflation in Britain. Some expressions of time have already been underlined. Underline all the others that you find. Make sure you include the preposition that goes with each expression. Then read the article again, looking for expressions of increase (↑) and decrease (↓). Record some of the expressions on the opposite page. Add more expressions from other articles of your own. Use the expressions to talk about your own situation or graphs from articles or reports.

UK inflation hits post-1982 high

Inflation accelerated again last month to the highest level since 1982. Worse for the Chancellor is the fact that there are clear signs that it has yet to peak, and increases can be expected for several months to come.

The markets had expected a slight slow-down, but contrary to expectations yesterday's figures showed a 1.8% jump in the retail price index between March and April.

Housing costs, including rent and rates, and higher charges for gas and electricity accounted for about half the rise. An unexpectedly sharp rise in the price of petrol edged the year-on-year rate up from 7.9% in March to 8% last month.

The news is acutely embarrassing for the Government. The Chancellor has always made it clear that he expects his economic policy to be judged by its success in curbing inflation.

The figure, which is more than double the European average, provided ammunition for Mr Neil Kinnock.

"The year-on-year figure should have started to fall this month. The fact that it hasn't shows the extent of the mess that the government has made of its policies" he said.

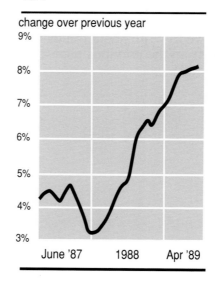

RPI

change over previous year

The latest rise brings inflation already to the peak forecast by Mr Lawson in his budget speech less than three months ago. Latest figures suggest further steady rises for some time before modest falls towards the end of the year.

Leading city analysts now seriously doubt whether there is any hope remaining of achieving the 5.5% annual rate forecast by the Chancellor in the Budget for the last quarter of the year. It is now thought that the annual rate could well exceed 7% at the end of the year after peaking at 8.5, or even 9%.

The underlying figures, excluding mortgage interest, also rose. In April last year the figure stood at 4.2%, but it had risen to 5.7% by March, it is now 5.9%.

The Government must be concerned as further price increases are already in the pipeline. Milk and travelling costs have just risen, and petrol has increased by a further 8 to 10 pence a gallon.

The RPI (base Jan. 87 100) rose to 114.3 from the March figure of 112.3.

GRAMMAR OF CHANGE 10

SPECIAL EXPRESSIONS 2

Record useful expressions for increase (↑) and decrease (↓) from the article opposite and other articles which you choose.

NOUN EXPRESSIONS	VERB EXPRESSIONS
a 1.8% jump	*accelerated*
↑	
↑	
↑	
a slight slowdown	*(should have) started to fall*
↓	
↓	
↓	

GRAMMAR OF CHANGE 11

COMPANY TRENDS

Describe economic trends in your company using some of the words below as the first words of your sentences. Try to use the change verbs and prepositions from the previous pages.

training	sales	costs	profits
exports	productivity	investment	morale
recruitment	turnover	wages/salaries	market share

Write true sentences about your present situation.

6

_____

_____

_____

_____

_____

_____

_____

_____

_____

_____

_____

_____

_____

_____

_____

_____

GRAMMAR OF CHANGE 12

NATIONAL TRENDS

Describe economic trends in your country using some of the words below as the first words of your sentences. Try to use the change verbs and prepositions from the previous pages.

taxes	earnings	crime	public spending
inflation	poverty	exports	quality of life
imports	interest rates	unemployment	the trade balance

Write true sentences about your present situation.

6

_____

_____

_____

_____

_____

_____

_____

_____

_____

_____

_____

_____

_____

_____

WORD FAMILIES 1

Some important professional words have a whole family of words which are related grammatically. Put one word in the centre and try to find four grammatically related words. You will only find a useful family if you have **at least one verb** and **one noun.** Often there will also be an adjective and one or more extra nouns.

Put the words at the end of the 'arms' of the diagram. Underline the part of the word which is most strongly stressed.

Add words which often make word partnerships with each member of the family.

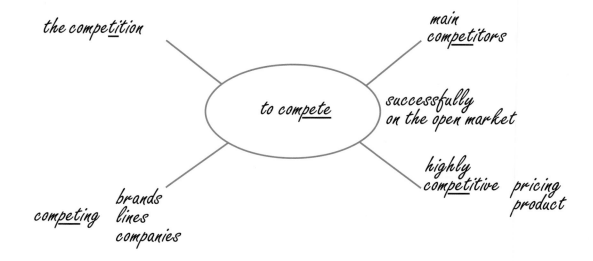

the compe<u>ti</u>tion

main
compe<u>ti</u>tors

to com<u>pete</u>

success<u>fully</u>
on the open market

highly
com<u>pe</u>titive   pricing
product

brands
competing   lines
companies

Write sentences about your own situation using different members of the word family.

_____

_____

_____

_____

_____

_____

_____

_____

6

WORD FAMILIES 2

Some important professional words have a whole family of words which are related grammatically. Put one word in the centre and try to find four grammatically related words. You will only find a useful family if you have **at least one verb** and **one noun.** Often there will also be an adjective and one or more extra nouns.

Put the words at the end of the 'arms' of the diagram. Underline the part of the word which is most strongly stressed.

Add words which often make word partnerships with each member of the family.

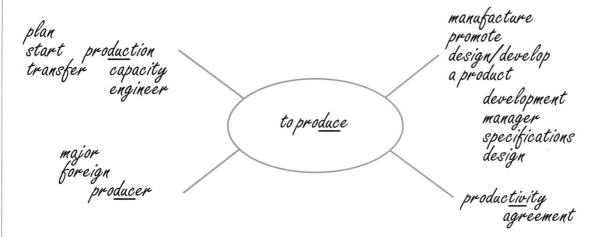

6

Write sentences about your own situation using different members of the word family.

_____

_____

_____

_____

_____

_____

_____

_____

_____

WORD FAMILIES 3

Some important professional words have a whole family of words which are related grammatically. Put one word in the centre and try to find four grammatically related words. You will only find a useful family if you have **at least one verb** and **one noun.** Often there will also be an adjective and one or more extra nouns.

Put the words at the end of the 'arms' of the diagram. Underline the part of the word which is most strongly stressed.

Add words which often make word partnerships with each member of the family.

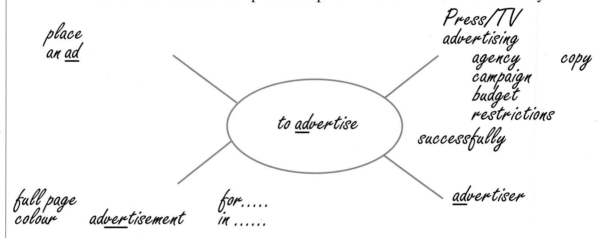

place
an _ad_

Press/TV
advertising
    agency   _copy_
campaign
budget
restrictions
successfully

to _advertise_

advertiser

full page
colour   ad_ver_tisement   _for_.....
_in_ ......

Write sentences about your own situation using different members of the word family.

_____

_____

_____

_____

_____

_____

_____

_____

_____

WORD FAMILIES 4

Some important professional words have a whole family of words which are related grammatically. Put one word in the centre and try to find four grammatically related words. You will only find a useful family if you have **at least one verb** and **one noun.** Often there will also be an adjective and one or more extra nouns.

Put the words at the end of the 'arms' of the diagram. Underline the part of the word which is most strongly stressed.

Add words which often make word partnerships with each member of the family.

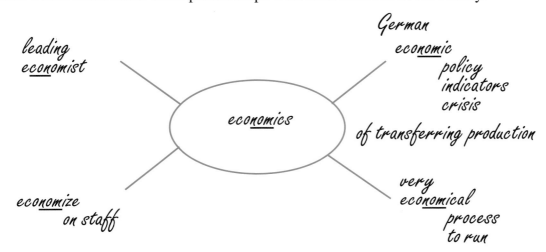

6

Write sentences about your own situation using different members of the word family.

_____

_____

_____

_____

_____

_____

_____

WORD FAMILIES 5

Some important professional words have a whole family of words which are related grammatically. Put one word in the centre and try to find four grammatically related words. You will only find a useful family if you have **at least one verb** and **one noun.** Often there will also be an adjective and one or more extra nouns.

Put the words at the end of the 'arms' of the diagram. Underline the part of the word which is most strongly stressed.

Add words which often make word partnerships with each member of the family.

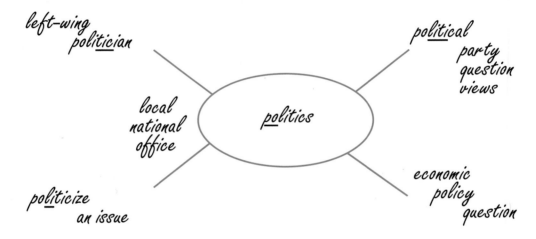

left-wing
poli<u>ti</u>cian

po<u>li</u>tical
party
question
views

local
national
office

po<u>li</u>tics

poli<u>ti</u>cize
an issue

eco<u>no</u>mic
policy
question

Write sentences about your own situation using different members of the word family.

_____

_____

_____

_____

_____

_____

_____

_____

6

WORD FAMILIES 6

Some important professional words have a whole family of words which are related grammatically. Put one word in the centre and try to find four grammatically related words. You will only find a useful family if you have **at least one verb** and **one noun.** Often there will also be an adjective and one or more extra nouns.

Put the words at the end of the 'arms' of the diagram. Underline the part of the word which is most strongly stressed.

Add words which often make word partnerships with each member of the family.

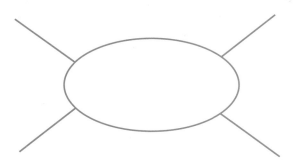

Write sentences about your own situation using different members of the word family.

_____

_____

_____

_____

_____

_____

_____

6

WORD FAMILIES 7

Some important professional words have a whole family of words which are related grammatically. Put one word in the centre and try to find four grammatically related words. You will only find a useful family if you have **at least one verb** and **one noun.** Often there will also be an adjective and one or more extra nouns.

Put the words at the end of the 'arms' of the diagram. Underline the part of the word which is most strongly stressed.

Add words which often make word partnerships with each member of the family.

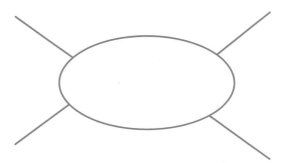

Write sentences about your own situation using different members of the word family.

_____

_____

_____

_____

_____

_____

_____

_____

WORD FAMILIES 8

Some important professional words have a whole family of words which are related grammatically. Put one word in the centre and try to find four grammatically related words. You will only find a useful family if you have **at least one verb** and **one noun.** Often there will also be an adjective and one or more extra nouns.

Put the words at the end of the 'arms' of the diagram. Underline the part of the word which is most strongly stressed.

Add words which often make word partnerships with each member of the family.

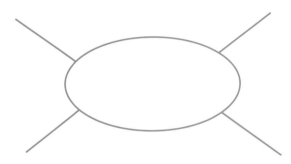

Write sentences about your own situation using different members of the word family.

_____

_____

_____

_____

_____

_____

_____

_____

Remember it will help you to feel comfortable using new language if you record it on cassette tape and listen to yourself saying the new language from time to time.

BUSINESS VERBS 1

Very often in business discussions you will need verbs to talk about communication, words like **ask, agree, advise.**

If you do not want to make unnecessary mistakes you need to know which words and structures can follow these verbs. You can list these in two columns, for example:

ASK	
	someone for something
	someone to do something
	someone if....
	someone when/how/why....

Use a business dictionary to check how the verbs listed on these pages are used. List in two columns. Write personal examples to make the meaning clear and memorable. Remember to write some questions as well as statements. Later cover one column and try to remember all the combinations in the other column.

It is easier to list the structures if you use:

SO. to mean **someone.** You can put in any name, company etc.

STH. to mean **something.** You **must** put in a noun.

From time to time recall a recent meeting, discussion or phone call. Imagine you are reporting it to someone else. Use some of the verbs on these four pages to describe your conversation.

ACCEPT	STH. (AN offer)	We accepted their revised offer immediately.
	THAT	We accepted that our marketing was not very strong in Spain.
	SO. FOR STH.	We accepted him for the sales reps. job.
ADVISE		
AGREE		

6

BUSINESS VERBS 2

Continue your list of important communication verbs. Look back often to check what you have recorded.

CONFIRM

CONSIDER

EXPLAIN

INVITE

OBJECT

OFFER

ORDER

6

BUSINESS VERBS 3

Continue your list of important communication verbs. Look back often to check what you have recorded.

6

POINT OUT	
PROPOSE	
QUERY	
RECOMMEND	
REFUSE	
REJECT	
REMIND	

BUSINESS VERBS 4

Continue your list of important communication verbs. Look back often to check what you have recorded.

REPLY

RESPOND

6

SAY

SPEAK

TALK

TELL

WONDER

HAVE 1

One of the most important verbs in English is 'have'. It is used in many special expressions. List useful expressions you notice on the key-word diagrams. Write example sentences for the most important examples for you.

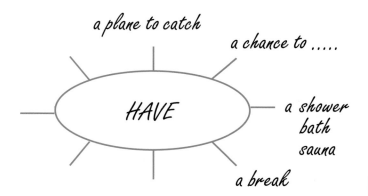

6

EXAMPLE SENTENCES

_____

_____

_____

_____

_____

_____

_____

_____

_____

_____

_____

HAVE 2

Complete the key-word diagram and write personal example sentences.

6

EXAMPLE SENTENCES

_____

_____

_____

_____

_____

_____

_____

Note that British and American English are often different here. Many of the things you 'have' in British English (a shower, a break) you 'take' in American English. Listen for examples when you are talking to native speakers of British or American English.

TWO-WORD VERBS 1

English has a lot of two-word verbs. They are very important in natural spoken English. List important verb-preposition combinations in the four columns below and opposite. Test yourself by covering different parts of the tables and recalling the covered words.

You will find it helpful to use a business dictionary to find combinations using these verbs:

BRING, BUY, CARRY, CATCH, DEAL, GET, GIVE, GO, HOLD, KEEP, MAKE, PAY, PULL, PUT, RUN, SELL, SET, TAKE, TURN.

BASIC VERB	PREPOSITION	WORD PARTNERSHIP	MEANING (English/Your language)
back	up	an argument	support
back	out of	an agreement	withdraw from
break	into	a market	penetrate
break	off	negotiations	halt/stop
break	up	a company	separate into parts

6

TWO-WORD VERBS 2

BASIC VERB	PREPOSITION	WORD PARTNERSHIP	MEANING (English/Your language)

6

TWO-WORD VERBS 3

On the previous two pages was one helpful way to list and revise these words which are very important, particularly in spoken English. On this page, put either a **verb** in the centre and add partnerships on the arms (*break off, break up...*) or put the small word in the centre and different verbs on the arms (*pick up, step up...*).

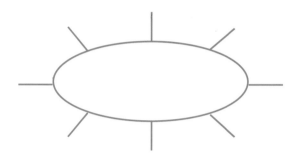

Write useful word partnerships and example sentences.

_____

_____

_____

_____

_____

_____

_____

_____

_____

_____

_____

_____

TWO-WORD VERBS 4

On the earlier pages (110/111) was one helpful way to list and revise these words which are very important, particularly in spoken English. On this page, put either a **verb** in the centre and add partnerships on the arms (*break off, break up...*) or put the small word in the centre and different verbs on the arms (*pick up, step up...*).

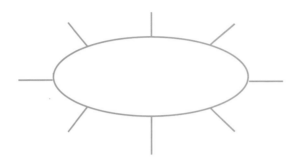

Write useful word partnerships and example sentences.

_____

_____

_____

_____

_____

_____

_____

_____

_____

_____

_____

TWO-WORD VERBS 5

On the earlier pages (110/111) was one helpful way to list and revise these words which are very important, particularly in spoken English. On this page, put either a **verb** in the centre and add partnerships on the arms (*break off, break up...*) or put the small word in the centre and different verbs on the arms (*pick up, step up...*).

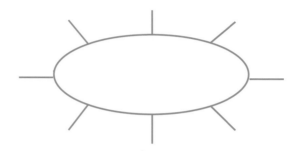

Write useful word partnerships and example sentences.

_____

_____

_____

_____

_____

_____

_____

_____

_____

_____

TWO-WORD VERBS 6

On the earlier pages (110/111) was one helpful way to list and revise these words which are very important, particularly in spoken English. On this page, put either a **verb** in the centre and add partnerships on the arms (*break off, break up...*) or put the small word in the centre and different verbs on the arms (*pick up, step up...*).

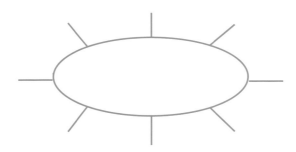

6

Write useful word partnerships and example sentences.

_____

_____

_____

_____

_____

_____

_____

_____

_____

_____

_____

_____

_____

BUSINESS PREPOSITIONS 1

Use these key-word diagrams to list useful examples of words which follow particular prepositions.

6

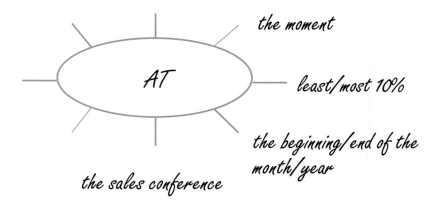

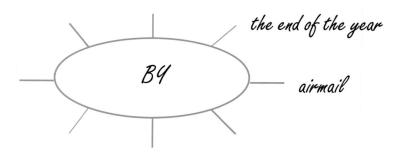

BUSINESS PREPOSITIONS 2

Complete these key-word diagrams to list words which follow the preposition.

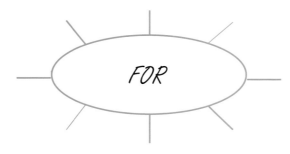

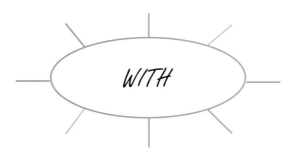

6

BUSINESS PREFIXES 1

A very convenient way to make extra use of some of the words you already know is to add to their meaning with a prefix. Complete the key-word diagram, then write sentences about your own situation.

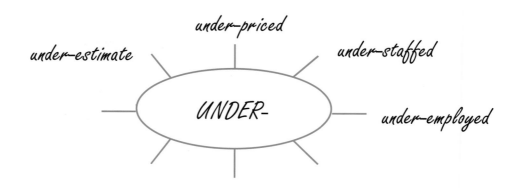

EXAMPLE SENTENCES

_____

_____

_____

_____

_____

_____

_____

6

BUSINESS PREFIXES 2

Complete the key-word diagram, then write sentences about your own situation.

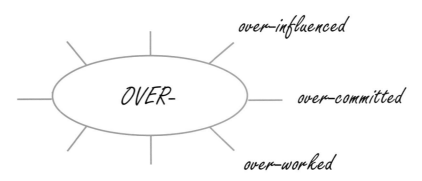

6

EXAMPLE SENTENCES

_____

_____

_____

_____

_____

_____

_____

_____

IMPORTANT MISTAKES 1

Not all mistakes are important. The most important ones are:

> if someone will misunderstand you
> if you give the wrong impression, for example, by sounding rude
> your typical mistakes—things you often get wrong.

Make a list of your important mistakes on these two pages. Cross out the wrong language. From time to time, cover the right hand column, and check that you can remember the correct English.

WRONG	CORRECT
I saw him ~~to~~ go.	I saw him go.
~~I have no possibility to come.~~	I'm afraid I won't be able to come.

IMPORTANT MISTAKES 2

WRONG	CORRECT

6

IMPORTANT MISTAKES 3

Businesses need accounts and so do people learning languages. Accountants use pages divided into columns to record and analyse figures. We suggest you do the same with common mistakes. Many mistakes occur when you make an 'impossible' combination of words. They are another example of the importance of word partnerships. Often 'correcting' a mistake means choosing a good word partnership instead of an impossible one. Look at these examples. In each one, underline a word combination which you think is wrong:

We discussed about the meeting.

I told to them the results.

I am staying on the Hilton.

I have been in the company since two years.

Can you explain me why?

Prices are higher in England as in Germany.

Each 'mistake' is an 'impossible' combination of words. You can list the correct form in two columns like this:

DISCUSS	STH. (WITH SO.)
TELL	SO. STH.
STAY	AT (a hotel) WITH (a family)
SINCE	(A POINT IN TIME) 1987/I left college/the war.
EXPLAIN	TO SO. why/when/how....

This table shows you the type of word which usually follows a particular word. Cover the right hand column and check yourself by making sentences with the words on the left, remembering the type of word which follows. In this way you can make your own grammar practice, and help avoid your most frequent mistakes.

List the correct partnerships you need, based on your frequent mistakes on the opposite page. Then check by covering the words in the right hand columns.

IMPORTANT MISTAKES 4

List the correct partnerships you often need here, using the two column system explained opposite.

6

WORD CONTRASTS 1

Many typical mistakes happen when you confuse one word or phrase with another. These can be 'false friends' (a word in your language is similar to the wrong English word), or two English words which are similar but used in different ways. On the following pages you will find some important word contrasts. Write two sentences for each pair, showing the correct use of each word. Write one above the line, and one below it. Check your examples are correct if you are unsure. Use the blanks to record other important word contrasts of your own in the same way. Check by covering the right-hand column and recalling the correct examples.

6

THERE
_____
THEY'RE

THERE
_____
THEIR

WILL
_____
WANT

I LIKE
_____
I'D LIKE

WORD CONTRASTS 2

Write two correct sentences, one above and one below the line. Use the blanks to do the same for your own word contrasts.

SAID

TOLD

_____

_____

OFFER

INVITE

_____

_____

LIVE

STAY

_____

_____

_____

_____

_____

_____

_____

_____

6

WORD CONTRASTS 3

Write two correct sentences, one above and one below the line. Use the blanks to do the same for your own word contrasts.

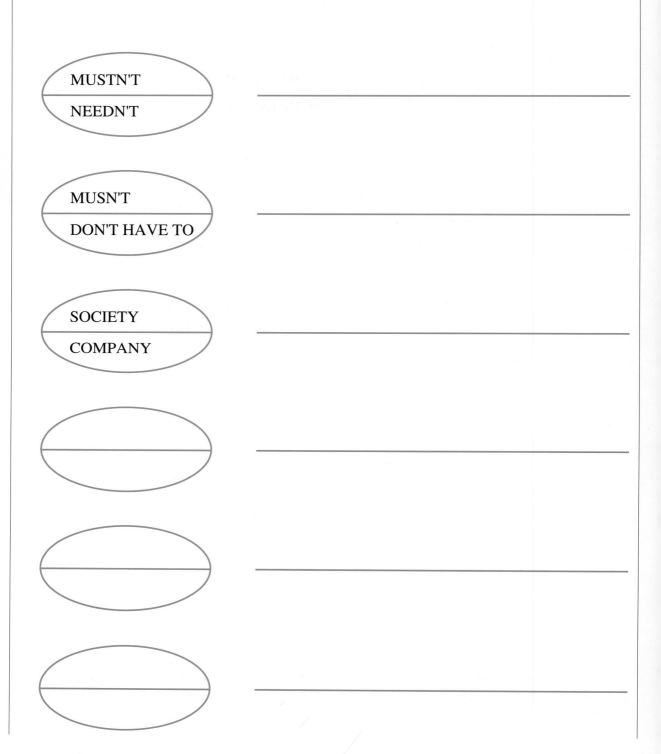

6

MUSTN'T

NEEDN'T

MUSN'T

DON'T HAVE TO

SOCIETY

COMPANY

POSSIBILITY AND NECESSITY

We often need to talk about what is possible or necessary, but in English these words are not very common. We use other words, called modal auxiliaries, to talk about these ideas.

The sentences on the left are unusual or unnatural. Match each sentence with one of the sentences on the right.

1. It's possible for him to go.   **a. He can't go.**

2. It's not possible for him to go.   **b. He may go.**

3. It wasn't possible for him to go.   **c. He has to go.**

4. It's not necessary for him to go.   **d. He should go.**

5. It's necessary for him to go.   **e. He needn't go.**

6. It's possible that he went.   **f. He was able to go.**

7. It's possible that he didn't go.   **g. He couldn't go.**

8. It's not possible that he went.   **h. He shouldn't go.**

9. It's a good thing for him to go.   **i. He must have gone.**

10. It's a bad thing for him to go.   **j. He can't have gone.**

11. It's certain that he went.   **k. He may not have gone.**

12. It was possible for him to go   **l. He may have gone.**
    and he went.

6

Write your answers in this table:

1	2	3	4	5	6	7	8	9	10	11	12

R emember to check later by covering the right hand column. Make sure you can say all the sentences in the right hand column naturally.

YOUR WORK SITUATION

ACCOMPLISHMENTS

I We (Your company)	have	started finished succeeded in decided to arranged to agreed to	_____ _____ _____ _____ _____ _____

CURRENT ACTIVITIES

I am We are	considering planning discussing preparing	_____ _____ _____ _____ _____

CURRENT ARRANGEMENTS

I am We are	seeing meeting going to launching	_____ _____ _____ _____ _____

(Say *when* in each case)

UNREALISED PLANS

I We The company	was were	going to	_____ _____ _____ _____	but	_____ _____ _____
	could have should have				

Notice that each form of the verb has a particular use to describe certain situations in business English.

Check later by covering part of the page and recalling the whole sentences.

6

INTRODUCTION

Every professional has different language needs, but it is possible to identify some language which is useful to most professional people. In this section you will find that language arranged so it is easy for you to find what you need. It is also easy to add some words of your own so that you can make this professional language useful for you personally.

This section contains the following:

Giving a presentation

Telephone language

Numbers and Symbols

Professional meetings

Important verbs

7

GIVING A PRESENTATION 1

If you are going to give a presentation of your company, a new product or system, you must provide the content of your talk. But using some of these professional phrases will provide a structure for your presentation and make it easier for your audience to follow what you say.

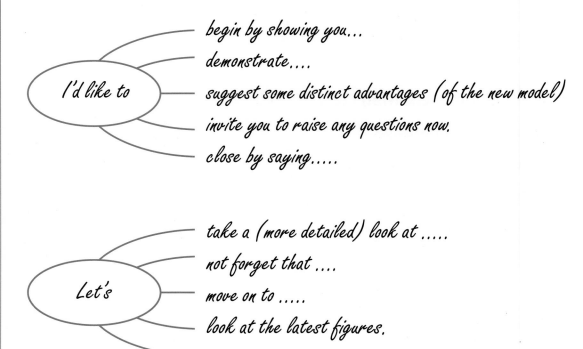

I'd like to
- begin by showing you...
- demonstrate....
- suggest some distinct advantages (of the new model)
- invite you to raise any questions now.
- close by saying.....

Let's
- take a (more detailed) look at .....
- not forget that ....
- move on to .....
- look at the latest figures.

Write some sentences you could use in a presentation of your own.

_____

_____

_____

_____

_____

_____

_____

GIVING A PRESENTATION 2

These professional phrases will help you to structure a presentation in English. Make sure you know how each one is used. It might help to add translations.

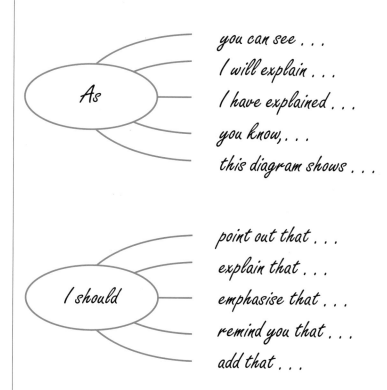

As
- *you can see . . .*
- *I will explain . . .*
- *I have explained . . .*
- *you know, . . .*
- *this diagram shows . . .*

I should
- *point out that . . .*
- *explain that . . .*
- *emphasise that . . .*
- *remind you that . . .*
- *add that . . .*

Write some sentences you could use in a presentation. Remember that writing your own sentences will make it easier to remember the important language. If you need to make a presentation, it will help to write full notes, and to include these phrases, not just the language you need to talk about your own business. Recording the presentation and listening to yourself will help you to feel more confident when you give the presentation to a real audience.

7

TELEPHONE LANGUAGE 1

There are a few expressions which are standard on the telephone. Here are the most useful:

INTRODUCTION

This is ..... Could I speak to Mr(s) ..... please?

Speaking. (when you are the person someone asks for. It means 'That's me')

Just a moment, please. I'll put you through.

MESSAGES

Could I leave a message, please?

Could you ask him/her to call me back, please?

Would you like to leave a message?

Shall I ask him/her to call you back?   Has (s)he got your number?

REQUESTS ABOUT THE PHONE

Could I use your phone, please?

Could I call my office, please?

Could you get me the number/code for ....., please?

REQUESTS ON THE PHONE

Could I speak to ...?

Extension (four seven three) please.

Could you tell (....) that (your name) called, please?

NEGATIVE RESPONSES

I'm afraid (s)he's   not in the office at the moment.
out for lunch.
in a meeting.
on holiday.
rather tied up at the moment.
no longer with us. Can someone else help you?
on another line.

Remember how important **I'm afraid** is in giving negative responses. (See page 29)

7

TELEPHONE LANGUAGE 2

In many places in this book we explain how important word partnerships are. The most important word for talking about the telephone is **call**. It can be a noun or a verb. It makes lots of important partnerships. Here are the most useful.

a local call	**to call (someone) back**
a long-distance call	**to call the office**
to pay for the call	**to call my wife/the office**
Can I call direct?	**to call New York/Tokyo**
I'm in a call box.	**I'll call you next week.**

Here are some more important 'telephone' words and expressions.

The line is engaged.

The line is out of order.

It's a very bad line. Can I call you back?

Have you the code for (Milan) please?

The receiver is off the hook.

I'm sorry, I think you must have the wrong number.

I'm afraid there's no one of that name here.

FINISHING A CALL

Sometimes it is difficult to show you are ready to finish. Many British people pause, then say **"Anyway....."** followed by another short pause. It gives the other person a chance to add something if they want and to show they are ready to finish too. Often if you are asked about something you finish with **"Right, I'll get back to you soon/next week/as soon as I can"**.

NUMBERS

British people usually give telephone numbers one digit at a time, except for 'doubles':

327904	**three two, seven nine, oh four**
226433	**double two, six four, double three**

Note: American 'telephone talk' is sometimes different from British English. The most important difference is a fixed expression with two completely different meanings:

A British operator says *"Are you through?"* to check you are successfully connected. Your call has just **started.**

An American operator says *"Are you through?"* to check that you have finished what you wanted to say. Your call has just **finished.**

7

NUMBERS AND SYMBOLS 1

Most business people need to say certain numbers, symbols and abbreviations. Here is a list of important ones. Say them several times so they feel comfortable when you say them.

YOU WRITE	YOU SAY
3/8	three eighths
0.27	nought point two seven
304	three oh four (for hotel rooms, notice '0' is usually 'oh')
1992	nineteen ninety two (for the year)
6 June	the sixth of June
6.30pm	six thirty p.m. or half past six (in the evening)
13%	thirteen percent

WEIGHTS AND DIMENSIONS

3cm x 8cm	three (centimetres) by eight (centimetres)
$3m^2$	three square metres
2kg.	two kilos
$^1/_2$lb.	half a pound (notice the 'a')
3cu.m.	three cubic metres
£2/kg.	two pounds per kilo

ABBREVIATIONS

These are said one letter at a time. Here are a few with their meanings.

plc	public limited company
fob	free on board
TVA	French VAT (Value added tax)
EC	European Community (sometimes called 'The Common Market')
USSR	The Soviet Union (often, wrongly, called 'Russia')

NUMBERS AND SYMBOLS 2

Each person has different needs for the signs, symbols and abbreviations that will be most important to them. Use these headings to list the ones which will be most use to you.

Spell your name, your company name, address etc.

Give important phone numbers naturally (see page 133)

Important products   Finance   Organisations

YOU WRITE	YOU SAY

PROFESSIONAL MEETINGS 1

If you are at a meeting with several people present, it will help you to present your ideas if you use the natural expressions which structure your contribution. Check the expressions on these two pages. Make sure you understand how they are used. Choose the ones you feel comfortable with. Say them several times. Record them, then listen to yourself.

BEGINNING

I'd like to make several points . . . firstly . . .
I'd like to begin by . . . ing.

ASKING FOR AN OPINION

What's your opinion of . . .
What's your position/view on . . .

GIVING AN OPINION

I believe/think/feel that . . .
In my opinion/view . . .

AGREEING

I agree entirely/completely.
I think we are in agreement on that.

AGREEING PARTIALLY

I would tend to agree with you on that.
I agree with you on the whole, but . . .

DISAGREEING TACTFULLY

I agree up to a point, but . . .
To a certain extent I agree with you, but . . .
I'm sorry but I really can't agree with you on that.

INTERRUPTING

If I may just interrupt you for a moment, I'd like to . . .
I don't want to interrupt, but can I just say that . . .

PROFESSIONAL MEETINGS 2

TAKING CONTROL OF THE DISCUSSION

Could I come in there for a moment, please?

Could I just make a few comments, please.

SAYING NOTHING

I'm afraid I can't comment on that yet/at this stage.

It's very difficult to say (at the moment).

MISUNDERSTANDINGS

I'm afraid there seems to be some misunderstanding . . . . Perhaps I can clarify what I said . . .

BLOCKING

I can see a lot of difficulties with that suggestion/proposal.

Could you explain in a little more detail, please.

I'm still rather unhappy about . . .

EXPRESSING YOUR VIEWS

That suggestion/proposal has my full support.

I suggest/propose that . . .

Don't you agree that . . . needs to be considered?

We would be happy to . . . if you were willing to . . .

I (particularly) want to emphasise/highlight the fact that . . .

CLOSING

To sum up, . . .

Finally, . . .

Let me conclude by stressing once again/saying . . .

M ake sure you feel comfortable saying these expressions before you try to use them in an important business meeting.

IMPORTANT VERBS 1

Often the words which you think are most important for you are nouns, for example, **meeting, sales, insurance**. But if you want to speak English you need to speak and write sentences. So, you need to know which verbs are often used with your important nouns and with word partnerships which include the noun. Here are some examples:

attend a meeting	**organise a meeting**	**postpone a meeting**
increase sales	**achieve a sales target**	**launch a sales campaign**
take out insurance	**pay an insurance premium**	**make an insurance claim**

These two and three-word combinations are often the basis of complete sentences in business English.

A good business English dictionary will help you with the important nouns but very often it does not help you to choose the correct verb to make important word partnerships. On the following pages is a list of some of the verbs which are often used in professional English. You can use the list in two different ways:

1. Take a key word. Look for verbs which are often used with the keyword. List the most useful word partnerships.

2. Choose an area of professional English, for example **banking, insurance,** or **exports.** Look for verbs which will make word partnerships connected with that area. Make a list, with equivalents in your own language.

On the opposite page you will see an example. All professionals need to talk about **meetings.** But which **verbs** do you need to help you to do this. The most important ones are listed.

Use the following pages to make similar lists starting from the key words or professional areas which **you** need.

7

IMPORTANT VERBS 2

Most professionals need to talk about meetings. You almost certainly know the word. But which verbs make word partnerships with it? A business dictionary and the verb list on pages 144 to 146 will help you to find partnerships and equivalents in your own language. Check later by covering the English column to make sure you can remember.

ENGLISH   YOUR LANGUAGE / EXAMPLE

address a meeting

arrange a meeting

ask for a meeting

attend a meeting

avoid a meeting

be late for a meeting

be tied up in a meeting

call a meeting

cancel a meeting

chair a meeting

close a meeting

have a meeting

interrupt a meeting

organise a meeting

postpone a meeting

report on a meeting

set up a meeting

start a meeting

take the minutes of a meeting

wind up a meeting

7

IMPORTANT VERBS 3

Choose a **key word** and write it here: _____

Use the verb list on page 144 / 6 and a business dictionary to find useful word partnerships.

List them with equivalents in your language or English examples.

WORD PARTNERSHIPS	YOUR LANGUAGE / EXAMPLE
_____	_____
_____	_____
_____	_____
_____	_____
_____	_____
_____	_____
_____	_____
_____	_____
_____	_____
_____	_____
_____	_____
_____	_____
_____	_____
_____	_____
_____	_____
_____	_____

7

IMPORTANT VERBS 4

Choose a **key word** and write it here: _____

Use the verb list and a business dictionary to find useful word partnerships.

List them with equivalents in your language or English examples.

WORD PARTNERSHIPS	YOUR LANGUAGE / EXAMPLE

7

IMPORTANT VERBS 5

Write a **professional area** useful to you here: _____

Use the list and a business dictionary to find and list useful word partnerships with equivalents in your own language or English examples.

WORD PARTNERSHIPS   YOUR LANGUAGE / EXAMPLE

7

IMPORTANT VERBS 6

Write a **professional area** useful to you here: _____

Use the list and a business dictionary to find and list useful word partnerships with equivalents in your own language or English examples.

WORD PARTNERSHIPS	YOUR LANGUAGE / EXAMPLE

7

LIST OF IMPORTANT VERBS

The following verbs are all common in professional English. Verbs which are marked * are verbs which are often used as part of two-word verbs like **take on, set up.**

A

Absorb	accept	account for	accumulate	achieve
acknowledge	acquire	add	address	adjust
adopt	advertise	afford	advise	agree
aim	allocate	allow	analyse	announce
apologise	apply	appoint	appreciate	approach
approve	argue	arrange	ask	assemble
assess	assist	attempt	attend	attract
audit	authorise	avoid		

B

Backdate	balance	bank	bargain	base
beat	become	begin	believe	benefit
bid	blame	block	book	boost
borrow	break*	bring*	budget	build
buy				

C

Calculate	call*	campaign	cancel	capitalise on
capture	carry*	centralise	chair	change
charge	chase	cheat	check	choose
claim	clear	close	collaborate with	collect
combine	commit	communicate	compare	compensate
compete with	complain	compromise	con	concede
conclude	conduct	confirm	confuse	congratulate
connect	conserve	consider	consign	consult
consume	contact	continue	contract	control
convert	copy	correct	cost	cover
credit				

D

Damage	date	debit	decide	declare
decline	deduct	defeat	defend	deflate
delay	delegate	delete	deliver	demand
demonstrate	demote	de-nationalise	depart from	deposit
depreciate	depress	de-regulate	design	describe
detail	devalue	develop	direct	discover
discuss	dismiss	dispatch	display	dissolve
distinguish	diversify	divide	downgrade	draft
draw up	drop	duplicate		

E

Earn	economise	elect	employ	enclose
encourage	endorse	enforce	enquire	enter
entertain	equip	escape	establish	estimate
evade	evaluate	exceed	exchange	exclude
execute	exercise	exhibit	expand	expect
expire	explain	export	express	extend
extract				

7

LIST OF IMPORTANT VERBS

Face	fail	fake	fall	falsify
favour	fax	feel	fetch	fiddle
figure out	fill in	finalise	finance	find
fine	finish	fix	float	fly
fold	follow	force	forecast	forget
form	forward	freeze	fulfil	fund
furnish				

Gain	gather	gear	generate	get*
give*	go*	govern	grant	greet
group	grow	guarantee	guess	

Haggle	halt	hand in	handle	harm
hedge	help	hire	hit	hold*
hurry	hurt			

Implement	imply	import	impose	improve
increase	incur	indicate	inform	inflate
influence	inherit	insert	insist on	inspect
instal	instruct	insure	integrate	intend
interfere with	interpret	introduce	invent	invest in
investigate	invite	invoice	issue	

Join	joke	judge		

Keep	know			

Label	launch	lay off	lead	learn
lease	leave	legalise	lend	license
lift	limit	link	listen to	loan
lock	lose	lower		

Mail	maintain	make*	man	manage
manufacture	market	maximise	mean	measure
meet	merge	minimise	miscalculate	mismanage
misunderstand	modify	move	mortgage	motivate
multiply				

Nationalise	neglect	negotiate	net	nominate
note	notice	notify	number	

Object to	obtain	offer	offload	omit
open	operate	oppose	order	organise
outbid	outdo	outsell	outvote	own
overcharge	overestimate	overheat	overvalue	overwork

Pack	package	patent	pay*	peak
peg	penalise	penetrate	perform	permit
persuade	phone	pick*	pin down	place

7

LIST OF IMPORTANT VERBS

plan	plough back	point out	pollute	post
predict	prefer	prepare	present	press
pretend	prevent	price	print	privatise
produce	prohibit	promote	prompt	propose
protect	provide	publicise	publish	purchase
Qualify	question	queue	quote	
Raise	rally	reach	react	read
realise	reassure	recall	receive	recognise
recommend	reconcile	record	recover	recruit
re-cycle	redeem	re-distribute	re-draft	reduce
refer to	refund	refuse	register	regret
regulate	release	rely on	remain	remember
remind	remove	renew	rent	re-organise
re-pay	repeat	replace	reply	report
re-possess	represent	request	require	rescue
research	reserve	resign	resist	resolve
respect	restrict	re-structure	retain	retire
return	re-value	review	revise	roll over
run*	rush			
Satisfy	save	say	schedule	secure
sell*	send	separate	settle	shake up
share	shelve	ship	show	shut down
sign	simplify	sink	slash	slow
smuggle	soar	solve	sort out	specialise in
specify	speculate	spend	split	spread
stabilise	staff	stamp	standardise	start up
state	stay	steal	stick to	stock
store	streamline	strike	structure	study
subcontract	submit	subscribe to	subsidise	succeed
sue	suffer	suggest	suit	supervise
supply	support	survey		
Talk	take*	target	tax	telephone
telex	tell	terminate	test	top up
trade	train	transfer	translate	transport
travel	trust	turn*	type	
Under-charge	undercut	undermine	undervalue	underwrite
understand	up-date	upgrade	use	utilise
Value	vary	verify	view	vote
Want	warn	warrant	waste	weigh up
welcome	win	wind up	withdraw from	withhold
work*	work out	wreck	write	
Yield				

7

INTRODUCTION

Successful international business means communicating with people from different cultural backgrounds. People not only have different language backgrounds, but also very different cultural backgrounds. We all look at the world from the perspective of our own culture. Often we are surprised that other cultures have very different perspectives. These differences can be exciting and stimulating — part of the reason for visiting foreign countries on holiday. They can also be puzzling and frustrating — 'Why do **these people** always say one thing and do something completely different?'. Sometimes in international business a breakdown in communication happens and neither side really knows what has gone wrong or why it has gone wrong.

Obviously, if you are planning to do a lot of business with one particular foreign culture, it is useful to learn as much as possible about ways of doing business in that culture. Some points may be 'easy to learn' — in the Christian world offices are usually closed on Sundays, but in the Moslem world on Fridays. Other points may be more 'difficult to learn' — in Britain it is not usual for two businessmen to embrace each other on meeting but in some Latin American cultures it is.

If you are planning to do business cross-culturally the most helpful first step is to learn more about **your own** cultural assumptions. The way we accept as the **normal** way of approaching a situation may in fact be very bound to our own cultural background. The purpose of these pages is to help you focus on basic assumptions about everyday business situations. We hope that the exercises will raise many questions in your mind. It is best to approach a foreign culture with an open and questioning mind.

8

TIME

Doing business involves organising time. Ways of organising time differ a lot from culture to culture. At what time should you meet? How long should a meeting last? etc. Check your assumptions here. Mark the **Yes** or **No** box for each question.

	YES	NO
It would be unusual for me to have a first business appointment before 9.30am.	☐	☐
I often organise a business lunch for 11.30.	☐	☐
My business lunches normally last about $1\frac{1}{2}$ hours.	☐	☐
I normally expect to stay in the office until about 6.30pm.	☐	☐
I never make business phone calls before 9am.	☐	☐
I stay in the office to work after the office closes quite often.	☐	☐
If a business partner arrives 10 minutes late for an appointment this is no real problem.	☐	☐
If I am invited for drinks to a business partner's home for 8pm I would usually arrive at 8.05.	☐	☐

Do you feel that your choices are very different from the choices a person from another country would make? Have you ever had any particular problems arising from different attitudes to time?

DRESS

Choice of dress is of course a personal matter. But it is also influenced by national culture, company culture and occupational culture. Check your own ideas here. Mark the **Agree** or **Disagree** box for each statement.

	AGREE	DISAGREE
I always wear a dark suit when attending a business meeting.	☐	☐
During a meeting I often take my jacket off.		
a) to be more comfortable.	☐	☐
b) to create a more relaxed atmosphere.	☐	☐
Wearing good quality, expensive clothes for important meetings is essential.	☐	☐
Sometimes it may be quite appropriate to wear smart casual clothes for a meeting.	☐	☐
I usually try to wear one item of clothing which carries the name or logo of my company.	☐	☐
If a business partner suggested going for a swim or a sauna together I would		
a) be surprised.	☐	☐
b) feel uncomfortable and refuse.	☐	☐
If I am invited to a business partner's home for a meal I would wear the same type of clothes as to the office.	☐	☐

8

When doing business internationally have you noticed any major differences between your dress assumptions and those of your partners? If there have been differences have you ever felt uncomfortable because of these?

BUSINESS MEETINGS

Not everybody does business in the same way. Some differences are personal but some are cultural. It helps if you have thought about what you expect and if you understand that people from other countries may have different expectations.

Which of the following topics might you talk about during a **first business meeting** with people from a new company that you hope to do business with regularly in the future?

In a $3\frac{1}{2}$ hour meeting how much time could be given to each topic that you choose? Complete the table with **your** expectations.

Pricing

Products or services

The architecture of the host's city

The weather

Sport

Family and private interests

Previous business experience in the country

TOPIC	TIME

Are there any other topics you would definitely expect to discuss in a first business meeting? If so, include them in the table with an estimate of the time you would give to each topic.

NEGOTIATION

Most professional people have to take part in negotiations from time to time. Of course, different people negotiate in different ways. It is partly a matter of personality. But we also make assumptions which are part of our background – about the way things are 'usually' done. But this often only means 'usually done where I come from'. Check your assumptions here. Mark the **Yes** or **No** box for each question.

In a negotiation do you:

	YES	NO
Get to know and use the first names of the people from the other side to establish a good climate?	☐	☐
Have periods of silence to think about the issues?	☐	☐
Use 'bargaining' techniques to arrive at a mutually acceptable price?	☐	☐
Ever say (the single word) 'No'?	☐	☐
Include unnecessary conditions so you can seem helpful and reasonable when you drop them.	☐	☐
Continue important, substantive discussions in a social setting, for example a restaurant?	☐	☐
Try always to get a written, signed agreement – in other words, a contract?	☐	☐
Include technical and legal specialists in your negotiating team?	☐	☐

8

Do you think the choices you have made are the same choices that people from another company or another country that you do business with would make? Have you ever felt uncomfortable because of the way others negotiated with you? Can you say why?

ORGANISATIONS

Every professional needs to be organised, but not everyone sees organisation in the same way. Different cultures have different values. These values affect the way we think and work in organisations. Check your own ideas. Mark the **Agree** or **Disagree** box for each statement.

	AGREE	DISAGREE
In an organisation, managers should be able to answer all their subordinates' questions.	☐	☐
In an organisation, group work is generally more productive than individual work.	☐	☐
Achieving power in an organisation is as important as achieving business objectives.	☐	☐
Conflict is a negative factor in organisations.	☐	☐
It is important for everyone in a company to know exactly who is reponsible for what. Everyone needs to know the company structure clearly.	☐	☐
As far as possible a company should treat all its employees, from the least to the most important in a similar way.	☐	☐
The most effective organisations include **both** women and men side-by-side in their management structure.	☐	☐
Companies should have a way of finding out what subordinates really think of their boss(es).	☐	☐

How many of the answers you have given are typical for **most** business people in your country? Do you think your international business colleagues would give the same answers?

8

PRESENTATIONS

There are of course many factors which influence the style of a **Presentation:** what is the purpose of the presentation, how many people are in the audience, how 'formal' is the overall situation? etc. Another significant factor is the country and culture where the presentation is being made.

Check your own assumptions here. When you give a presentation in **your** culture, which of the following do you do? Choose and put in sequence. If any steps are missing add them in yourself.

Tell a joke.

Make a general statement about the subject.

Refer to visuals.

Ask the audience to introduce themselves.

Ask questions.

Summarise.

State your objectives.

Smile at the audience.

Take your jacket off.

Look serious to inspire confidence.

8

From your own experience of attending presentations have you noticed any major differences in national styles?

FORMAL MEETINGS 1

The language used in formal meetings is very standard. The same expressions are almost always used.

On these two pages we usually give two expressions in each section. The first is the standard formal use; the second is more informal but still used in meetings conducted in the formal style. The sections marked * are for use by the Chairman.

In all cases, instead of *Chairman* some people now prefer to use *Chairwoman*, or *the Chair*. In a formal meeting we suggest you agree which use the people at the meeting, particularly the person in the chair, prefer.

OPENING *

Ladies and Gentleman, I declare the meeting open.
Right, shall we get started.

MINUTES *

Would someone move that the minutes of the last meeting be accepted?
Can we take the minutes as read?

AGENDA *

Has everyone received a copy of the agenda? The first item is . . .

INVITING A SPEAKER *

(Mr Barnard), would you like to say something about this?
Have you anything to say, (John).

ASKING TO COMMENT

Excuse me, Mr Chairman, may I say something, please?
Could I just say something here, please.

FINISHING AN AGENDA ITEM *

Has anyone anything else they wish to add before we move on to the next item on the agenda?
Has anyone anything further to add?

CONTROLLING THE SUBJECT *

I don't think that is relevant at the moment. The main question is . . .
Let's not get side-tracked. Could you stick to the subject, please?

NAMING A SINGLE SPEAKER *

We can't all speak at the same time. Would you like to comment first, Mrs Hill?

8

FORMAL MEETINGS 2

MOVING ON *
Could we move on to item (3) on the agenda?
Can we go on now to...

POSTPONING DISCUSSION *
If nobody objects, I suggest we leave this matter until (our next meeting/a later date.)
Perhaps we could leave this for the time being. We can come back to it later.

PROPOSING
I'd like to propose that . . .

SECONDING
(Chair) Would anyone like to second that?
(Others) Mr Chairman, I'll second that motion.

ANNOUNCING A VOTE *
Perhaps we should take a formal vote on this. Can I ask for a show of hands?
Could we take a vote on that?

VOTING * (All formal for the Chair)
Those in favour of the motion, please?
Those against?
Any abstentions?
The motion is carried unanimously/by six votes to three.

The motion has been rejected overwhelmingly/by six votes to three.

AGREEING WITHOUT A FORMAL VOTE *
Can I take it everyone is in favour of that, then?
Are we all agreed on that?

ANY OTHER BUSINESS *
Is there any other business?
Any further points (anyone wants to bring up)?

CLOSING THE MEETING *
I declare the meeting closed. Thank you everybody.
That's all for today. Thank you.

You may find it helpful to think about some of the questions on pages 150 and 151 if you have to attend formal meetings conducted in English.

CASE STUDY 1

Mike Brown is a recently appointed project manager with Western Paints — a US company with subsidiaries around the world. The job is giving him his first experience of managing a culturally diverse group. His project team consists of two Americans, a Japanese, a Swede and an Italian. Mike himself is American.

At a recent meeting of the group Mike gave an outline of some proposed deadlines and tasks. "A lot of work has to be done during these next two weeks," he explained. "It means we will have to work over the weekend in order to finish this important report. Let's now divide up the work and then go away and do it."

Mike was surprised when Sven Lindberg, the Swedish member of the group, seemed unhappy about working over the weekend. Another problem was that both Takahiro Miki (Japanese) and Marco Venditti (Italian) were unsure about how to do their parts of the report.

Mike believes that he is a good manager of people. He has been responsible for many different groups of people in the United States and has never had any real problems in motivating people to work.

On the Friday evening after the meeting he went home and talked about the situation with his wife. "I just don't know the best way to motivate these foreigners," he said. "Maybe they want me to organise a party for them — make them feel good. We'll have a meal here in our house one evening and invite them all."

So Mike and his wife Carol organised a dinner party for the group members and their wives. Everyone came but nobody seemed to enjoy themselves very much. It was very difficult to find topics of conversation to interest people — unusual for Mike. Marco's wife spoke only a little English which was another problem. All the guests left quite early and Mike was not very optimistic about the next day at work.

Have you been in any situation like this?

What do you think is the problem?

Do you think the reactions of Mike, Sven, Takahiro and Marco will be the same? If not, why not?

8

CASE STUDY 2

Can you match the comments with the people? Can you give reasons for your choices?

Sven Lindberg

Marco Venditti

Mike Brown

Takahiro Miki

	WHO?	WHY?
"Mike Brown should make more decisions. He's the manager. He's not paid to ask us questions. We need to know what to do."		
"I can't work with people who have a 'nine-to-five' approach."		
"These Americans are only interested in doing the job. What about my family? It's not fair to them if I have to work in my free time."		
"I don't like the responsibility of writing this report myself. Why can't we do it as a group? After all we are a project team."		
"Why should I call him 'Mike'? I'm not interested in parties in his house. He's my boss not my friend!"		

8

Have you worked with any Swedes, Japanese, Italians or Americans yourself? Were they "typical"?

STEREOTYPES

As Mike Brown has discovered there are often problems in managing a multinational team of people. For example the American emphasis on the individual is very different from the Japanese wish to work as a member of a group. The Swedish desire to balance business and private life may give Americans the idea that they are not committed to work. For some cultures home and culture are clearly separate. Inviting colleagues to your home may not be seen as a welcoming gesture.

Choose **one** of the following cultural groups. Do not choose your own culture. Write 5 or 6 words that you think describe the members of this culture.

Americans   **Italians**   **British**   **Swedes**   **Japanese**

National Group	

Now choose a national group that your company often does business with. Write some words to describe that nationality.

National Group	

How many of your descriptions are positive words? How many are negative? Very often our **stereotypes** are negative and not positive. This can be dangerous if it influences our decisions.

Now write the names of 3 of your **foreign business partners** here. Also their nationalities. Are they "typical"?

_____   _____   _____

Stereotypes can be dangerous. If you work with multinational groups it is important to learn as much as possible about the cultural expectations of the members. In this way differences can become **advantages** and not disadvantages.

DIFFICULT SITUATIONS

Difficult situations are even more difficult when doing business with people from other cultures. They may not recognise your 'signals'. You may not recognise their signals.

Check some of your ideas here. Mark the **Yes** or **No** box for each statement.

	YES	NO
When people mean "No" I expect them to say "No", politely but directly.	☐	☐
I like to stay relatively silent when a business partner is explaining a proposal. This shows that I am interested and respect their ideas.	☐	☐
If they won't call me by my first name then they probably don't like my ideas and don't really want to build a business relationship.	☐	☐
The words people use are so important that it is necessary to agree everything in writing.	☐	☐
The best way to show a deal has been agreed is to have a drink together.	☐	☐
If I am one of four people at a business dinner, I expect to pay a quarter of the bill.	☐	☐

If you disagreed with any of these statements, what was **your** expectation? Do you think other nationalities would have very different expectations?

8

This book cannot give answers for how every different culture thinks about different situations. The **Cultural Background** pages are to help you to understand that what **you** expect may be quite different from what **other people** expect. It is easier to avoid misunderstandings if you realise in advance that they might happen.

THE DEPARTMENT OF TRANSPORT

Survey of crew accommodation in merchant ships

Instructions for the guidance of surveyors

London: Her Majesty's Stationery Office

© Crown copyright 1989
First published 1989

ISBN 0 11 550899 6

HMSO publications are available from:

HMSO Publications Centre
(Mail and telephone orders only)
PO Box 276, London, SW8 5DT
Telephone orders 01-873 9090
General enquiries 01-873 0011
(queuing system in operation for both numbers)

HMSO Bookshops
49 High Holborn, London, WC1V 6HB   01-873 0011 (Counter service only)
258 Broad Street, Birmingham, B1 2HE   021-643 3740
Southey House, 33 Wine Street, Bristol, BS1 2BQ   (0272) 264306
9-21 Princess Street, Manchester, M60 8AS   061-834 7201
80 Chichester Street, Belfast, BT1 4JY   (0232) 238451
71 Lothian Road, Edinburgh, EH3 9AZ   031-228 4181

HMSO's Accredited Agents
(see Yellow Pages)

and through good booksellers

Contents

CHAPTER 1

General

1.1 Object of Instructions

1.1. These instructions are issued by the Department of Transport for the guidance of their Marine Surveyors in surveying the crew accommodation of merchant ships for the purposes of the Merchant Shipping Acts and the Merchant Shipping (Crew Accommodation) Regulations 1978 and subsequent Amendments thereto* hereafter referred to as the Regulations. They are intended to supplement the Regulations in matters of detail to ensure uniformity in treatment. They also indicate to shipowners, shipbuilders and others the procedures which the Department adopts for the survey and acceptance of crew accommodation.

1.1.2 The Regulations take account of the provisions of:

.1 the International Labour Convention (No 92) concerning Crew Accommodation on board ship, the text of which is contained in the Report of the 32nd Session of the International Labour Conference, 1949 (Cmd 7852), and

.2 the International Labour Convention (No 133) concerning Crew Accommodation on board ship (Supplementary Provisions), the text of which is contained in the Report of the 55th Session of the International Labour Conference, 1970 (Cmd 4800), and

.3 the International Labour Conference Recommendation (No 140) concerning Air Conditioning of Crew Accommodation and Certain Other Spaces on board ship, the text of which is contained in the Report of the 55th Session of the International Labour Conference, 1970 (Cmd 4800).

1.2 Layout

The practice of repeating of the actual wording of the Regulations has not been adopted however, wherever considered necessary the relevant Regulations Number and sub-para is referred to, with expressions and terminology interpreted, for ready cross reference.

---

* Merchant Shipping (Crew Accommodation) (Amendment) Regulations 1979 SI 1979 No 491;
  Merchant Shipping (Crew Accommodation) (Amendment) Regulations 1984 SI 1984 No 41;
  Merchant Shipping (Crew Accommodation) (Amendment) Regulations 1989 SI 1989 No 184

1.3 Application of Regulations

See Regulation 3 noting that with reference to:

.1 Regulation 3 the expression 'or which is at a similar stage of construction' means the stage at which:

.1.1 construction identifiable with a specific ship begins; and

.1.2 for that ship, assembly has commenced comprising not less than 50 tons or 1 per cent of the estimated mass of all structural material, whichever is the less.

.2 Regulation 3(3) in the expression 'but which has been reconstructed or substantially altered':

.2.1 're-constructed or substantially altered' relates to alterations or major repairs carried out as a result of pre-planning and not as a result of accident or emergency, and

.2.2 'substantially' governs the word 'altered' and therefore altered should be taken to apply to the ship in general and not only to the crew accommodation. Thus a substantial alteration of a ship not involving the crew accommodation, as for example lengthening, would bring the ship within the scope of Part I of the Regulations, while on the other hand a considerable rearrangement of the crew accommodation which did not involve substantial alteration or reconstruction might not render the ship subject to Part I of the Regulations. In the latter case, however, the Surveyor should press for compliance with the requirements of Part I of the Regulations where he considers it to be practicable taking into account the extent of the rearrangement.

Where the Surveyor has any doubt as to whether or not alterations or repairs are such as to bring a ship within the scope of Part I of the Regulations, the case should be referred to Marine Directorate DSG1c for guidance.

1.4 Definitions

In these Instructions the following definitions apply:

'Department' means the Department of Transport;

'Regulations' means the Merchant Shipping (Crew Accommodation) Regulations 1978 as amended;

'suitable material' means a material approved by the Department, or acceptable to a Department Surveyor for the purpose proposed and being in compliance with all relevant requirements;

'Surveyor' means a surveyor appointed by the Department;

'crew' means all persons including the master employed under contract in any capacity on board a ship;

'Passenger' means any person on a ship who is not a crew member on that ship and is more than one year old.

2

1.5 Law Relating to Crew Accommodation

The principal statutory provisions affecting crew accommodation are in section 20 of the Merchant Shipping Act 1970 and the Merchant Shipping (Crew Accommodation) Regulations 1978 as amended.

1.6 Application for Survey

The builder, owner or owner's agent of a ship for which survey of the crew accomodation is required should make application for survey to a Mercantile Marine Office on Form SUR 6. The application should be accompanied by a fee estimated to cover the survey and where appropriate the surveyor's expenses. At the conclusion of the survey the actual fee should be calculated and the balance collected or a refund made, as appropriate.

1.7 Exemptions from the Regulations

It should be noted that no provisions for exemption have been included in the Regulations because the Department can grant exemptions from the requirements of the Regulations under section 20(4) of the Merchant Shipping Act 1970.

.1 In considering exemption(s) from the Regulations the Department is obliged to consult not only with the shipowners/shipbuilders but with the trade unions of the crew, all in accordance with the Conventions referred to in paragraph 1.1.

.2 Annex 4 and 5 gives an outline of the procedures to be followed with regard to exemptions.

.3 In the case of small ships of the order of 200 gross tonnage or less where the granting of specified exemption(s) would be clearly impracticable, it may be agreed in consultation with Marine Directorate DSG1c that the vessel should be the subject of an overall exemption provided applicable safety and health standards are complied with and that the best practicable degree of compliance with the Regulations is achieved. In such cases an 'as fitted' General Arrangement plan will require to be submitted in duplicate for approval and stamping on completion of which one copy is to be sent to the owner together with a document of exemption SURVEYS 185A/79.

1.8 Maintenance and Inspection

See Regulation 38 noting also that:

.1 On every occasion when a ship is registered or re-registered, or when it has been substantially altered or reconstructed, the surveyor should inspect the ship and satisfy himself that the crew accommodation complies with the requirements of the Regulations.

.2 On receipt of a complaint by a seafarer's organisation or by a member of the crew of a ship; the Surveyor should visit the ship and if, on inspection, the crew accommodation is found not to comply with the Regulations, should notify the defects to the owner, owner's agent or master as the case may be. The Surveyor should also instigate follow-up action to ensure compliance with the requirements of the Regulations.

.3 Surveyors should also carry out ad hoc inspections of crew accommodation
   .3.1 as opportunity arises, in order to satisfy themselves that the requirements of the Regulations are being complied with, if they are not so satisfied, they should proceed as indicated in the preceding sub-paragraph.
   .3.2 in association with 'Port State Control' and 'General Inspection' surveys.

.4 A record of inspection of crew accommodation carried out as required by the Regulations is to be entered in the ships official log book as required by the Merchant Shipping (Official Log Book) Regulations 1981 (SI 1981 No 569).

1.9 Contraventions

In accordance with section 20(6) of the Merchant Shipping Acts 1970 and 1979 and the Criminal Penalties etc (Increase) Order 1984 the owner or master of a ship is liable, if the provisions of the Regulations are contravened, to a fine not exceeding £2,000 and the ship, if in the United Kingdom, may be detained.

1.10 Other Regulations, Codes, Standards and Merchant Shipping Notices relevant to matters covered by these Regulations

Below are given listings under the relevant group headings valid October 1988, however it is recommended that the latest indexes are checked to ensure that the references given have not been amended, superseded or revoked and that no further relevant requirements or recommendations have been produced.

Statutory Instruments

1975 No 2220 Merchant Shipping (Crew Accommodation) (Fishing Vessels)

1978 No 795 Merchant Shipping (Crew Accommodation) Regulations

1979 No 491 Merchant Shipping (Crew Accommodation) (Amendment) Regulations

1984	No 41	Merchant Shipping (Crew Accommodation) (Amendment) Regulations
1988	No 1637	Merchant Shipping (Means of Access) Regulations
1988	No 1641	Merchant Shipping (Safe Movement on Board Ship) Regulations
1981	No 569	Merchant Shipping (Official Log Books) Regulations
1986	No 144	Merchant Shipping (Medical Stores) Regulations
1988	No 1547	Merchant Shipping The Merchant Shipping (Medical Stores) (Amendment) Regulations
1979	No 1435	The Public Health (Ships) Regulations 1979
1984	No 408	Merchant Shipping (Health and Safety: General Duties) Regulations
1972	No 1871	Merchant Shipping (Provisions and Water) Regulations
1972	No 1872	Merchant Shipping (Provisions and Water) (Fishing Vessels) Regulations
1980	No 529	Merchant Shipping (Radio Installations) Regulations 1980
1980	No 569	Merchant Shipping (Official Log Books) Regulations 1980
1985	No 1664	Merchant Shipping (Protective Clothing and Equipment) Regulations

NB. See also latest Merchant Shipping Notice 'Principal Acts and Regulations on Merchant Shipping'.

Merchant Shipping Notices

662	List of Crew
776	Inspection of Ships' provisions under the Merchant Shipping Acts
782	Polyurethane foam and other organic foam materials
837	Inspectorate of ships' provisions
847	Dry Cleaning Plants: requirements for installation and operation
908	Heating appliances burning solid fuel
946	Fires involving electric heating or drying equipment
980	Recommendations on the safe use of pesticides in ships (and Amendment)
1115	Ship provisions and indication of minimum durability
984	Use of Liquefied Petroleum Gas (LPG) in domestic installations and appliances on ships, fishing vessels, barges, launches and pleasure craft
1118	Fires in accommodation spaces of merchant ships
1150	The weekly inspection of crew and catering accommodation
1155	Asbestos—health hazards and precautions

1188	Good ship management
1194	The status of persons carried on United Kingdom ships
1195	Protective clothing and equipment regulations
1210	The Merchant Shipping (Medical Stores) Regulations 1986, SI 1986 No 144. Exemption from need to carry Scale 7 medical items aboard Class VI and Class VIa passenger vessels
1214	Recommendations to prevent contamination of ships' freshwater storage and distribution systems
1215	Contamination of ships' air conditioning systems by legionella bacteria
1216	The Ship Captain's Medical Guide (21st Edition)
1305	Code of Practice for noise levels on ships
1343	Merchant Shipping (Means of Access) Regulations 1988—Code of Practice
1344	Merchant Shipping (Safe Movement on Board Ship) Regulations 1988—Code of Practice

NB. See also latest Merchant Shipping Notice 'Merchant Shipping Notices current . . . .'

British Standards

BS MA1: Part 1:	1969 General Shipboard Services
BS MA1: Part 2:	1969 Ventilation
BS MA1: Part 3:	Sanitation
BS MA18: 1973(1980)	Specification for salt water piping systems
BS MA24: 1974	Specification for ships' side scuttles
BS MA25: 1973	Specification for ships' windows
BS MA94: 1981	Specification for thermal insulation for marine piping systems
BS MA101: 1986	Specification for toilet retention and recirculation systems for the treatment of toilet waste on small craft
BS MA103: 1956	Specification for the design conditions and basis of calculations for air conditioning and ventilation of accommodation spaces in ships
BS 853: 1981	Specification for calorifers and storage vessels for central heating and hot water supplies
BS 1597: 1975	Specification for limits of methods of measurement of electromagnetic interference generated by marine equipment and installations
BS 1945: 1971	Specification for fireguards for heating appliances (gas, electric and oil burning)

BS 2655: 1970	Specification for lifts, escalators, passenger conveyors and paternosters
BS 3052: 1958(1987)	Specification for electric shower supply units
BS 3456: Pt 2	Specification for safety of household and similar electrical appliances
BS 6920: 1988	Suitability

NB. See also latest BSI Standards Catalogue

International Maritime Organisation Publications

Noise Levels on Board Ships

Recommendation on the Safe Use of Pesticides in Ships

World Health Organisation Publications

Guide to Ship Sanitation

Guidelines for Drinking Water Quality

Miscellaneous Publications

Water Fittings and Materials Directory—issued annually by the Water Research Centre, Marlow, Bucks.

NB. See also latest IMO Publications Catalogue.

CHAPTER 2

Instructions in relation to specific regulations

2.1 Plans

See Regulation 5 noting that:

.1 On receipt of such plans they should be examined by a Surveyor to ensure that the requirements of the Regulations will be met. After examination the Surveyor should either:

    .1.1 indicate to the builder or owner in writing that the proposals meet the requirements of the Regulations, or where this is not the case indicate the deficiencies and/or the amendments required for compliance see also Annex 1; or

    .1.2 where the proposals involve policy for which the Surveyor is not in receipt of sufficient instructions refer the matter to Marine Directorate DSG1c for advice.

.2 In respect of sister ships, which the surveyor is dealing with jointly, a submission should be made for each ship, so that on completion the full history for each ship is contained on its relevant crew accommodation file.

.3 Any reasonable further plans or information required by the Surveyor to confirm that the arrangements, materials or equipment are in compliance with the Regulations and those Instructions shall be provided by the Owner, Builder or other relevant persons.

2.2 General Requirements

The general requirements are specified in Regulation 6.

Equipment, furniture, fittings etc should comply or be equivalent to the British Standard Specifications where these are relevant.

2.2.1 *Siting of Accommodation*
See Regulation 6(1) noting that:

.1 In ships where, by virtue of the design and operational features, such of the space below and above deck amidships or aft is needed to accommodate special facilities and storage space associated with the operation of the ship and which cannot be situated forward, the Department would consider it impracticable to provide accommodation amidships or aft. However, the Department would not expect difficulties to arise in providing accommodation amidships or aft in the majority of ships.

.2   The Regulation reference to the position of the accommodation in relation to the Summer LWL is mandatory. However, the Department is willing to consider granting exemption from this Regulation in the case of small ships and of ships not engaged in the carriage of cargo. Small ships are those of the order of 200 gross tonnage, while examples of non-cargo carrying ships are passenger only, tug, cable, salvage, crane or dredger type ships. Cargo being defined as under the Load Line Regulations.

2.2.2 *Noise Levels*
See Regulation 6(2) noting that:

.1   It is important that the crew accommodation be so sited as to provide as quiet an environment as practicable within that accommodation and in particular sleeping rooms should be sited so that the occupant or occupants, as the case may be, are not affected by undue noise originating either from spaces outside the confines of the crew accommodation or from other parts of the crew accommodation.

.2   Acoustic insulation shall be fitted where sleeping rooms are affected by local or ambient noise. Such insulation may also be necessary in respect of the hospital areas and where beds in sleeping rooms are positioned close to bulkheads separating such rooms from washing, sanitary and similar spaces.

.3   The desirable upper limits of noise in accommodation are specified in the Code of Practice for Noise Levels in Ships' published by and obtainable from Her Majesty's Stationery Office. The noise levels contained in this Code should be used for guidance by designers and wherever practicable noise levels should be within the limits specified.

.4   Guidance as to the responsibility for the measurement of noise levels on new and existing ships and the attendance of a Department Surveyor is given in the Code.

2.2.3 *Passageway Handrails*
With reference to Regulation 6(3)(b)(i), where a passageway exceeds 1 metre in width, a handrail should be fitted on one side. Where the width exceeds 1.8 metres, handrails should be fitted on both sides.

2.2.4 *Clear Headroom*
Regulation 6(4) specifies the clear headroom required at every point in a space where full and free movement is necessary. In this context Surveyors should pay particular attention to electric lights, ventilation trunks and any other local projections which might infringe on the clear headroom required.

2.2.5 *Sole Usage*
Regulation 6(5) prohibits the use of crew accommodation areas for the benefit of passengers. However given the areas concerned have been designed such that provisions for the crew are of no less a standard than that required by these Regulations the Department will consider applications for exemptions from this Regulation.

2.3 Divisions Between the Crew Accommodation and Other Parts of the Ship

See Regulation 7 which deals with this subject is some detail, relevant additional points to note are:

.1 In ships which trade or operate in cold climates the boundaries of accommodation should be protected against cold in a similar way to that in respect of protection from overheating.

.2 It should be noted that all insulation materials for use in accommodation spaces should be approved by the Department.

.3 In deciding what, if any, protective covering against condensation, is required, regard should be paid to the related approval documents, the standard of ventilation installed and any case put forward by the builders/owners.

2.4 Interior Bulkheads

See Regulation 8 noting that:

.1 With regard to Regulation 8(1) the Department will accept, subject to the requirements of the relevant Merchant Shipping (Fire Protection) Regulations as applicable, materials which have been specifically approved as suitable for the construction of internal bulkheads in crew accommodation. However, in sanitary accommodation, laundries, drying rooms, cold store rooms or dry provision store rooms any of the materials which the Department has specifically approved as suitable for the construction of internal bulkheads may be used subject to any materials which absorb water being suitably sealed and covered with hard faced plastic or other material impervious to water.

.2 Notwithstanding the above, and subject to Regulation 8(3), Regulation 8(2)(b) requires that boundary bulkheads of sanitary accommodation, laundries, drying rooms, galleys and cold store rooms should be watertight to the heights specified and hence steel, or where permitted under the relevant regulations, aluminium, should be used for this portion of the bulkheads. The watertight heights should be measured above the top of the deck covering in the 'wet space'.

.3 Boundary bulkheads of galleys, including doors and shutters, should be constructed of steel.

2.5 Overhead Decks

See Regulation 9 noting that:

.1 Regulation 9(1) provides three different methods for the protection of the crowns of any part of the crew accommodation which is exposed to weather. As far as the Department is concerned each of the methods is equally effective and hence the choice of which method should be used is for the builder and/or owner to decide.

.2 Schedules 1 and 2 of the Regulations set out the various qualities which deck covering and insulating materials for underside of deck should possess in order to comply with the Regulations. Before such materials may be used however they must first be approved by the Department.

.3 Details of deck coverings and insulating materials which the department has approved for such use and procedures for obtaining approval are specified in Annex 2 to these Instructions.

2.6 Floor Decks

See Regulation 10 noting that:

.1 Schedule 1 of the Regulations sets out the various qualities which deck covering materials must possess in order to comply with the Regulations.

.2 Details of deck coverings which the Department has approved and procedures for obtaining approval are specified in Annex 2 to these instructions.

.3 When considered practicable floor decks in officers' sleeping and dayrooms, and, in ships over 25,000 tons, in ratings' sleeping rooms, shall be provided with a fitted carpet which shall cover all exposed parts of the floor deck.

.4 Any carpet fitted shall be approved under the relevant Merchant Shipping (Fire Protection) Regulations and the Departments 'List of Approved Fire Resisting Materials' give details of such carpets. Other properties of the carpet such as durability, ease of cleaning, colour fastness and anti-static properties are at the owner's discretion.

.5 Owners are required to ensure that carpets fitted in crew accommodation will be kept clean. If this cannot be fulfilled carpets should be replaced when necessary.

.6 Although floor decks in sanitary accommodation, galley and laundries are required to be covered with terrazzo, tiles or other hard material it should be noted that no specific approval by the Department is required for these materials. Nevertheless the Surveyor should be satisfied that the finished covering is impervious to liquids, can be easily kept clean and provides a good foothold in addition to being generally satisfactory having regard to the space in which it is fitted. Therefore to assist Surveyors and in order to prevent materials being considered by the Surveyor as not suitable after they have been laid it is recommended that appropriate samples of the material be forwarded to him at the same time as the plan of floor covering is submitted. It should be noted that tiles referred to in Regulation 10(5) mean tiles of the ceramic type and not those made of plastic material of the PVC type.

2.7 Access and Escape Arrangements

See Regulation 11 noting that:

2.7.1 *General*

.1 In dealing with escapes from crew accommodation the Surveyor should also refer to the relevant Fire Protection Regulations which also deal with this subject.

.2 Particular care should be taken in the positioning of escapes. As a general philosophy it can be assumed that escapes will need to be used in the case of explosion or fire or in the case of physical damage to the ship caused by collision. It need not be assumed in planning escapes that fire and collision will occur simultaneously in different parts of the ship and therefore escapes need only to be strategically sited to cover one occurrence at a time.

.3 In the case of a ship where crew accommodation is situated below the weather deck, as is the case in some ships see para 2.2.1, it is preferable for the two means of escape from compartments between two main bulkheads to be by means of well sloped stairways. It is realised that this is not always practicable and in such a case, the escape arrangements will be acceptable provided that:

   .3.1 One of the escapes is by means of a stairway to the deck over and the other is by way of a readily openable doorway to an adjacent compartment provided that in the adjacent compartment there is a stairway leading to the deck over, or

   .3.2 One of the escapes is by means of a stairway to the deck over and the other is by ladder to an escape hatch (see sub-paragraph 2.7.6) to the deck over. It may be necessary to provide in addition to a stairway, two escape hatches, one port and one starboard so as to cover the whole block of accommodation being considered.

.4 Wherever possible stairways and ladderways should be arranged to be climbed in the forward and aft direction to provide the best opportunity for escape when the vessel is heeled. Doorways leading from the upper level of ladderways are preferable to exits provided by a hatch.

.5 Where accommodation spaces are arranged in several tiers, as is generally the case, the Surveyor should ensure that even though the lowest tier has two means of escape in a vertical direction, in subsequent tiers 'funnelling' of escapes does not occur so that in higher tiers there is virtually only one means of escape. Passageways and stairs shall be of suitable width to ensure ready transit of the maximum number of personnel anticipated.

.6 The means of escape should be sited as far away as practicable from each other, compatible with serving the compartment they are meant to cover and suitable in size or number and arrangement to ensure ready transit of the maximum number of personnel anticipated.

.7 See also paragraph 2.11.2(.4). Lighting from the alternative source of power should be suitably positioned along all escape routes.

2.7.2 *Blind Passageways*

Although every endeavour should be made to provide two means of escape from passageways it is of course realised that in isolated cases this may not be possible. Therefore for guidance in such cases a blind passageway *might* be considered as acceptable provided it is not longer than 5 metres in cargo vessels of less than 500 tons, 7 metres in cargo vessels of 500 tons or greater, 7 metres in passenger vessels carrying not more than 36 passengers and 13 metres in passenger vessels carrying more than 36 passengers. Even though a blind passageway meets the above criteria where such a passageway leads to messrooms, recreation rooms, cinemas or other communal spaces in which personnel congregate the arrangement should not be accepted unless additional satisfactory emergency escapes are provided from such spaces, see also paras 2.7.4, 2.7.6, 2.7.7 and 2.7.8.

2.7.3 Sleeping Rooms

It is necessary to provide an emergency means of escape from a sleeping room where access to such a sleeping room is by way of a dayroom, there being no direct access by means of a door to the sleeping room from a lobby or passageway. Ideally, the crew accommodation should be designed so that a sleeping room is so positioned that an emergency escape therefrom is not required. Where there is a need to provide an emergency means of escape from a sleeping room this should be achieved by fitting a clearly marked crash panel to an adjacent room or passageway or where this is not possible by fitting fixed steel rungs and grab rails on the outside of the structure in the vicinity of a fully opening window or a 400 millimetre diameter opening sidescuttle provided that the window or sidescuttle is not close to the waterline of the ship and that the fixed steel rungs lead to an open deck from which ready access to lifeboats or liferafts is available.

2.7.4 Messrooms, Recreational Rooms etc

In ships in which messrooms, recreation rooms, cinemas, television rooms and other communal spaces are provided to accommodate more than 15 personnel at any one time two doors should be provided to the adjacent passageway. In some ships, by virtue of the layout of the accommodation, it will not be possible to provide two doors to an adjacent passageway. In such cases in addition to the door to a passageway, a door to an open deck, or if this is not possible, an opening type window or 400 millimetre diameter sidescuttle(s) may be permitted in lieu provided that escape through the window or sidescuttle leads to an open deck from which ready access to lifeboats or liferafts is available.

2.7.5 Doors

All doors to crew accommodation should, in general, be of the hinged type. Where from space considerations it is not practicable to provide this type of door, a sliding door may be permitted provided it can readily be removed from the rail from either side of the space or that a crash panel is fitted in the door which can be 'kicked out' with a minimum of effort from either side. Intermediate doors in passageways should not be capable of being locked. The door handles and locks on all sleeping cabin doors should be of a type which allow the door to be opened from the inside without using a key even when locked from the outside.

2.7.6 Hatches

2.7.6.1 Where small hatches or trunks are used to provide an alternative means of escape they should be not less than 400 millimetres square. The hatch should not be capable of being locked and should be operable from below and above. Such a hatch should be provided with a counter-balance weight for ease of opening. Access to the hatch should be by means of a fixed steel ladder.

2.7.6.2   It should be ensured that hatches are so sited that they cannot be over stowed with deck cargo or stores or in the case of crew accommodation sited below vehicle decks in RO-RO ships that vehicles cannot be parked over them. In some cases it will be necessary for hatches to be sited on raised kerbs or be protected by tubular stanchions and rails. The painting of white lines is not to be accepted as the only means of protection to escape hatches.

2.7.7   *Escape Sidescuttles or Windows*
2.7.7.1   Opening type sidescuttles or windows can with advantage be provided in certain instances to effect an alternative means of escape. Sidescuttles provided for escape purposes should not be less than 400 millimetres in diameter and windows should be of the fully opening type of dimensions compatible with use as an escape. Where such a sidescuttle or window is locked by a cone nut to prevent unauthorised opening eg in lieu of mosquito protection on air conditioned ships, a special key should be placed in a glass box adjacent to the sidescuttle or window. Suitable notices should be displayed.

2.7.7.2   Escape sidescuttles or windows should not be allowed at the ship's side, or in structures in line with the ship's side, in

.1   positions close to the waterline, or

.2   positions such that the person escaping will be required to enter the sea. When escape sidescuttles or windows are accepted, fixed steel rungs should be provided which lead to an open deck from which ready access to lifeboats or liferafts is available.

2.7.8   *Crash Panels*
2.7.8.1   Crash panels can also in certain instances be used with advantage to provide an alternative means of escape. Nevertheless, an escape route should not involve more than one such crash panel.

2.7.8.2   The crash panel should be fitted so that it can be 'kicked out' with a minimum of effort and should be clearly marked to indicate its purpose. Where a crash panel is utilised to provide an escape to another compartment the Surveyor should ensure that the door to that compartment opens on to a passageway and is, under all conditions, capable of being opened from the inside.

2.8   **Pipes etc**

See Regulation 12 noting that:

2.8.1   Where steam pipes are permitted by regulation to pass through crew accommodation passageways the following precautions should be observed:

.1   If the steam supply from the boiler passes through a reduction valve, such valve should be of accepted design and suitably sited. Preferably, the valve should be situated in the engine room and not at the after steering gear.

.2 Copper is not considered a suitable material.

.3 The number of joints should be kept to a minimum and as far as is practicable, there should be no joints within the principal crew accommodation areas.

.4 All steam pipes and attachments should be designed for the maximum pressure of the ship's boiler system.

.5 The bends should be 'ordinary' bends with large radii, and not of the ogee type. Efficient drainage arrangements should be provided. A steam trap should preferably be fitted to the steam pipe at the lowest point. Drains should be connected to the exhaust steam line.

2.8.2 The regulation requires that both supply and exhaust steam pipes shall be 'properly encased' and in this connection efficient encasement in suitable insulation will be accepted as complying with this requirement. All flanges should also be fully insulated and covered.

2.8.3 Facilities for cleaning soil and waste pipes shall as far as practicable not be positioned in the accommodation spaces referred to in regulation 12(5). Where it is impracticable to comply with regulation 12(5) the joints should be suitably sited and no joints should be placed over:

.1 in messrooms—any table

.2 in sleeping rooms—any bed

.3 in dry provisions storerooms—any rack, shelf or bin required for the storage of provisions

.4 in galleys—any cooking range or any other piece of apparatus used for preparation or cooking of food or any food preparation space

.5 in hospitals—any bed

2.8.4 Where CO_2 pipes of fixed fire extinguishing systems pass through accommodation spaces, the Surveyor's attention is drawn to the requirements of the Departments 'Survey of Fire Appliances—Instructions for the Guidance of Surveyors'.

2.8.5 Plastic piping and associated fittings of a suitable type as listed and approved in the current Water Fittings and Materials Directory (revised annually and prepared by the Water Research Centre, Henley Road, Medmenham, PO Box 16, Marlow, Bucks SL7 2HD) may be used for domestic cold fresh systems, salt water systems, drains from washbasins, baths, showers, deck scuppers from sanitary accommodation and soil pipes subject to compliance with the appropriate regulations regarding structural fire protection and the structural and watertight integrity of the ship. However, plastic piping should not pass through machinery spaces, galleys or other heat producing spaces, nor should it be led within the boundaries of refrigerated chambers.

Plastic piping should be adequately but freely supported with suitable provision for expansion and contraction to allow for large movements between plastic piping and steel structures. Hot and cold water piping should be run sufficiently apart or be suitably insulated to avoid heat transfer.

2.9 Awnings

See Regulation 13.

Awnings should be constructed of canvas, other suitable fabric, aluminium or other rigid sheeting subject to the Surveyor's satisfaction. The use of non-combustible materials should be required as considered relevant eg in way of safety equipment. Since there is a risk of injury to personnel and damage to instruments and equipment by metal or other rigid sheeting which might work loose in a gale the Surveyor should be satisfied that the construction is adequate for gale conditions, paying particular attention to the need to provide efficient fastenings where the edges of the sheets overlap.

Notices should be displayed where rigid awnings are not suitable for walking on.

2.10 Heating

See Regulation 14 noting that:

2.10.1 *General*
Subject to the requirements of other relevant Merchant Shipping Regulations:

.1 where a combination of the various types or a novel design of heating system is proposed it will require to be specifically considered by the Department.

.2 Heating boilers should be effectively insulated, sited in a steel or equivalent enclosed and suitably ventilated compartment clear of the accommodation wherever practical. Doors to the compartment shall be self-closing steel arranged such that they are well clear of escape routes.

.3 Filling arrangements for fuel should be provided from open deck and storage facilities and capacity are to be to the Surveyors satisfaction.

2.10.2 *Central hot water heating installations*
.1 Should preferably be on the two pipe system. The flow pipe should be run at a sufficiently high level without long horizontal leads as far as may be practicable and ventilated independently of air cocks on radiators or on the circuits, except that these arrangements are not necessary where the water is circulated by means of a power operated pump or pumps. Except where pumps are provided to circulate the water, radiators should be kept off the floor, but no higher than necessary to provide a good slope for the return to the boiler in the worst condition of trim. Screw plugs or cocks should be fitted to each radiator to allow the radiator to be ventilated. A make-up tank of adequate capacity should be provided and should have a permanent connection, via turn-dish or similar, for automatically filling from the fresh water system. The fitting of a steam coil or anti freeze addative in the make-up tank to gravity fed systems is a means of ensuring maintenance of supply of the essential heating medium in ships which operate in cold climates and should be provided where the make-up tank is sited in an exposed position.

.2 Exposed pipes and tanks should be lagged or insulated and the maker's instructions and a diagram of the installation should be carried on the ship.

.3 If a single pipe system is used particular care should be taken to ensure that there is an adequate circulation head under the worst condition of trim, either by gravity or by a power operated pump or pumps.

2.10.3 *Steam systems*
Should be self-draining as far as is practicable and should be suitably vented and trapped where necessary. If a single pipe system is used, steam and condensate should flow in the same direction. There should be ample safeguard against overpressure.

2.10.4 *Radiators*
Should be provided with independent control and should be designed with a view to economy in space and uniformity in room temperature. In large rooms, there should be two or more radiators to ensure a reasonable uniform distribution of heat.

2.10.5 *Guards*
Of a suitable type should be fitted to prevent radiators with high surface temperatures coming into contact with the occupant or occupants of the space or coming into contact with bedding or other material which might accidentally fail and smother the radiator and cause a fire. Guards should always be fitted in way of electric radiators together with suitable notices e.g. 'DO NOT COVER'.

2.10.6 *Any Heating system*
Should be capable of producing the required temperature (from the ambient) within 24 hours, and central hot water systems should be capable of maintaining the required water temperature in the case of boilers using solid fuel with fires banked for a period of at least 6 hours, unless the fuel can be fed automatically.

2.10.7 *In Port arrangements*
Particulars of the arrangements for heating while the ship is in port should be agreed by the Surveyor.

2.10.8 *Testing on Completion*
The heating system and its ability to comply in full with all requirements should be demonstrated to the Surveyor on completion.

During test on board the ship

.1 doors, sidescuttles, windows and skylights may be kept closed.

.2 In the case of a ship provided with a heating system supplying warm air by means of a mechanically trunked ventilation system the ventilation system need supply only 25 cubic metres of fresh air per person per hour even though the system is capable of providing quantities of fresh air in excess of this figure.

.3 Mechanical ventilation systems, if fitted, should be in operation during the heating test.

.4 All natural ventilators should remain open unless extremely draughty conditions prevail when ventilators fitted with locally operated means of closing may be closed e.g. slides or hand wheels.

.5 The reduction in emissivity due to an increase in ambient temperature, and therefore room temperature, is allowed for in the following formula, which may be used to obtain the temperature required in the crew accommodation under test.

$T = 21.8 + 0.8t$

where T is required temperature in °C and where t is ambient temperature in °C

Note: The formula is only valid for ambient temperatures down to -1°C, if lower temperatures are anticipated in the normal operating schedule of the ship practical tests supported by heat calculations are to be agreed by the Surveyor.

.6 Temperatures should be taken in the centre of the space at approximately 1 metre above the floor using a suitable thermometer. An adequate number of spaces should be tested to ensure that the Regulations are complied with throughout the ship.

.7 All crew accommodation spaces which are required by the Regulations to be provided with means of heating should be inspected while the heat is being supplied, and particular attention should be paid to the hospital ward and to spaces subject to heat leakage from ventilation trunking, piping, machinery spaces, calorifiers, drying rooms etc.

.8 Where excessive temperatures are recorded, steps should be taken to ensure there will be no grounds for complaint on account of overheating.

.9 If, after test, radiators are painted with metallic paint or enclosed with shields, grilles or other means the Surveyor should carry out a further test unless there is obviously an adequate margin of performance.

2.11 Lighting

See Regulation 15 noting that:

2.11.1 Natural Lighting

.1 With regard to natural lighting the intensity of daylight varies considerably from summer to winter and therefore clear winter weather conditions are to be taken as a criterion.

.2 Natural lighting should normally be provided by side scuttles, windows or skylights. Skylights should not be placed over beds and should be weathertight. Although glass prisms may be used as aids to the primary sources of natural lighting their use is not recommended by the Department since they can be a constant source of trouble due to the difficulty involved in maintaining weathertightness.

.3 Sidescuttles and windows should be spaced and sited, so far as practicable, to be of maximum benefit to the occupants. In general, and wherever service conditions permit, sidescuttles or windows should be fitted whether skylights are fitted or not.

2.11.2 *Electric Lighting*

.1 Electric lighting can either be of the incandescent or fluorescent type; the latter normally gives a better standard of lighting with conservation of power.

.2 Surveyors when considering the number of lighting points, should seek to establish the disposition and the type of shade and fitting to be used, that the luminance provided is well diffused, and that glare and deep shadow are, so far as practicable, avoided. In the case of incandescent lighting unshaded bulbs and/or clear glass shades should not be used, except in the case of pearl lamps of 60 watts or lower power or in the case of other lamps having a finish giving equal diffusion.

.3 Individual lights should not in general exceed 100 watts having regard to any limitation indicated on the shade, although a higher figure may be accepted in a messroom or galley. Bed lights of 40 watts, tungsten filament are acceptable as satisfying the requirements of the Regulations in respect of the electric reading lamp for each bed.

.4 The Regulations require an efficient alternative lighting system or an alternative supply of electrical power to be provided. This requirement will be considered as being met if there are two generators provided or one generator together with storage batteries. Oil lamps will not be permitted, however Department approved constantly charged supplementary emergency lighting units may be considered for fitting on ships of less than 200 gross tonnage or in areas on larger ships where exemption has been granted from the requirement of the Regulations for natural light.

2.11.3 *Testing on Completion*

.1 For natural lighting the ability to comply in full with the Regulations should be demonstrated to the Surveyor on completion.

.2 It is preferable that electric lighting tests be carried out during the hours of darkness but they may be carried out during daylight provided suitable screens are used over sidescuttles, windows and skylights to prevent the ingress of daylight. The ability to comply should be demonstrated to the Surveyor on completion by means of a direct reading meter, the accuracy of which has been certified by a reliable authority.

.3 Surveyors should note that each Marine Survey Office has been supplied with electric light photometers for use in carrying out checks such photometers give direct reading in lux and cover the range of illuminance specified in Schedule 3 to the Regulations.

.4 Tests should be carried out using the ship's power and not shore supply.

.5 Test results should be prepared in tabular form by the builder or contractor and should contain the designation of the sample spaces tested, the wattage and number of lamps fitted, the illuminance required by Schedule 3 to the Regulations, and the illuminance recorded during test.

2.12 Ventilation

See Regulation 16 and Table 1, noting that:

TABLE 1—APPLICATION OF REGULATION 16

Gross tonnage	>1,000ᵀ	500–1,000	>500	Notes
Foreign going ships plying within lat 50°N and lat 45°S	Air conditioning (A/C) Reg 16 2(A) See note [1]	Mechanical ventilation (MV) Reg 16(4) See note [2]	MV Reg 16(4)	[1] Mech exhaust to sanitary spaces etc Reg 16(3) [2] Except if vessel operates in tropics or Persian Gulf
Ships regularly employed in tropics or Persian Gulf	A/C Reg 16 2(A) See note [1]	A/C Reg 16 2(B) See note [1]	A/C Reg 16 2(B) See note [1]	[3] Foreign air changes may be reduced by
Home trade	MV Reg 16(4) See note [3]	MV Reg 16(4) See note [3]	Nat Reg 16(7)	
Ships regularly engaged on New Zealand Coast		As home trade		
Ships operating north of lat 50°N		As home trade		
Ships operating south of lat 45°S		As home trade		

NB: HOME TRADE is defined as voyages between ports' located within the area bounded by a line from a point on the Norwegian coast in latitude 61° North to a point 61° North 02° West; thence to a point 58° North 10° West; thence to a point 51° North 12° West; thence to Brest, but excluding all waters which lie to the eastward of a line drawn between Kristiansand, Norway, and Hanstholm lighthouse on the North Danish coast.

2.12.1 General

.1 All crew accommodation spaces should be provided with exhaust ventilation even if situated on an open deck.

.2 If crew accommodation is sutated near heat producing spaces, the size and type of ventilator should receive special consideration in conjunction with the heat insulation in order to ensure a satisfactory rate of heat dissipation.

.3 Means should be provided, where necessary, to enable lengths of ventilation trunking to be cleaned internally.

.4 Where screening is required to prevent the admission of mosquitoes, it should be readily portable, or hinged, or able to slide into a position clear of the orifice. It should be noted that where screening is fitted to ventilation trunks it will be necessary to increase the inlet area of the trunks by approximately one-third above that required for ventilation purposes only.

.5 Ventilation trunking should as far as practicable be kept outside the confines of the propelling machinery casings. If this is not possible and ventilation trunks pierce propelling machinery casings, then the requirements of other relevant Merchant Shipping Regulations may apply. As a minimum the trunking within the casings should be constructed of steel, be adequately supported and the minimum thickness of plating should be 5 millimetres for a trunk 750 millimetres in width or diameter and 3.2 millimetres for 300 millimetres or smaller, thickness for intermediate widths being obtained by interpolation. The provision of fire resisting shutters in association with ventilation trunking of less thickness than specified is not to be accepted.

.6   Mechanical or air-conditioned ventilation systems should be designed to minimise bacterial growth. Intakes should be designed to minimise the risk of rain water being driven into filters and these should be readily accessible to enable cleaning of the washable type or replacement as necessary if of the fibreglass variety or similar. If the air intake to the system is from inside a ventilation machinery casing adequate drainage of the space should be provided if rainwater which may become stagnant is able to enter.

.7   In air-conditioning systems the cooler unit (de-humidifier) should be fitted with an efficient drain and the condensate sump should be capable of being cleansed to ensure that stagnant condensate cannot accumulate. If the face velocity over the cooler block is greater than 2 metres per second (400 feet per minute) an effective moisture eliminator should be fitted in the distribution air stream. The insulation of the air-conditioning unit plenum chamber should be fitted with a waterproof facing.

.8   Adiabatic spray type humidifiers are not acceptable as they are considered prone to generating air carried water droplets which may support bacteria etc.

2.12.2 *Natural Ventilation*

.1   All enclosed passageways from which air supplies are drawn should be provided with suitable inlet ventilators.

.2   The standard of natural ventilation required by the Regulations may be attained by a system of passageway ventilation with two cowl ventilators each having an area of not less than 0.002 square metres per person, with adequate openings at the top and bottom of the bulkheads dividing the rooms from the passageways, and an exhaust ventilator in each room. In the event of the ventilators in the rooms being shut down under draughty conditions, the heat of the rooms will be sufficient to ensure that the two passageway ventilators, functioning as inlet and outlet respectively, will maintain the air in the rooms in a satisfactory condition of purity.

.3   Supply cowl ventilators should be sited in positions exposed to the wind but as far as practicable sheltered from the sea so that they will be efficient for supply purposes.

.4   Special difficulties in fitting cowl type ventilators in small ships will be dealt with on their merits. It should be noted that experience has shown that the inflow of air through mushroom, goose-neck, torpedo or other similar type of ventilators is uncertain. Disc or butterfly ventilators should be fitted as inlets only to single or double berth sleeping rooms suitably situated on an open deck.

.5   Wherever ventilators open directly into a sleeping room, messroom, washplace, galley or pantry, means should be provided to regulate and diffuse the flow of air as widely as possible.

.6   The lead for ventilation trunks to any compartment should be as short and direct as possible, and the following requirements should be complied with:

    6.1   When ventilation trunks have curved bends or knees and the angles do not exceed 30° no additional area need be provided.

6.2 When ventilation trunks have curved bends or knees where the angle exceeds 30° the following additions to the area should be made:

.1 Curved bends—angles from 30° to 60°, add 5 per cent for each bend. Curved bends—angles from 60° to 90°, add 10 per cent for each bend.

.2 Knees—angles from 30° to 60°, add 16 per cent for each bend. Knees—angles from 60° to 90°, add 36 per cent for each bend.

Note: If the radius of the inner side of a bend is less than the diameter of the pipe, the bend is to be regarded as a knee. Alternatively, if difficulty is experienced in applying the above owing to space restriction, suitable 'splitters' may be fitted. When long vertical or horizontal ventilation trunks are fitted a suitable addition to the area should be made to allow for frictional losses.

2.12.2.1 HOSPITALS
See Regulation 35(11) noting that:

.1 The natural supply is to be trunked to within 300 millimetres above the floor.

.2 Where the hospital is, due to the design of ship, sited such that natural ventilation is not practicable other suitable back-up ventilation arrangements will be considered.

2.12.3 *Mechanical Ventilation*

.1 Where an owner desires a ship, which by regulation is required to be provided with mechanical ventilation to Schedule 4 requirements, to be air conditioned, then the Department will permit this arrangement and grant the necessary exemption from the specified air changes of Schedule 4, provided the air-conditioning arrangements comply with the requirements of the Regulations and these instructions (para 2.12.4).

.2 Paragraph 7 of Schedule 4 to the Regulations requires the speed of every supply fan to be capable of being varied where DC motors are used. This requirement will be considered as being met if the fan can operate at full speed and approximately two-thirds of full speed.

.3 From noise and vibration considerations if it is proposed to use fans of the propeller type in crew accommodation trunking, fans specially designed for the purpose should be fitted.

.4 Except when cooled air is delivered or when electric table fans are fitted in addition, louvres capable of delivering a jet of air controllable as regards volume and direction but not necessarily independently, should be fitted in all sleeping rooms, messrooms and washplaces. The position of any louvre should ensure an adequate air movement throughout the room in which they are fitted.

.5 Non-return nozzles or flaps should be fitted in supply trunking to water closets, store rooms and other spaces where effluvium may occur, unless supplied from independent branches. In the case of a hospital ward, washplace, galley or pantry, directional louvres should be fitted in supply trunking and non-return flaps should be used.

.6 The provision of a high standard of ventilation in dry provision store rooms necessarily sited over heat producing spaces will not justify omission of heat insulation unless a system of air-conditioning, including temperature and humidity control, is fitted.

.7 Suitable filters for the removal of dirt, dust or grease should be provided where the conditions of service make this desirable, for example galley exhaust systems. Fan inlets should be so sited and protected as to permit, as far as possible, the full operation of the fans in all weathers.

2.12.4 Air-conditioning
2.12.4.1 GENERAL
.1 It should be noted that in the case of ships in which the refrigerating machinery may be out of action when in port the system should be capable of maintaining the standards specified in Schedule 4 to the Regulations.

.2 It will be noted that British Standard BSMA 103: 1986 which is technically equivalent to ISO Standard 7547–1985 gives guidance on design conditions to be assumed and the basis of calculations for ships' air-conditioning systems. These design conditions are somewhat more onerous than those given in Regulations.

2.12.4.2 OVERALL REQUIREMENTS
.1 The air-conditioning system as a whole should be so designed that it is capable of maintaining the following conditions:

	Dry Bulb °C	Relative Humidity Per Cent	Derived Wet Bulb °C
Ambient	32	78	28.7
Internal	29	50	21.4

.2 When the internal conditions are specified against a different ambient temperature the Surveyor should ensure that relevant calculations are submitted to confirm that the system will be capable of maintaining the above conditions. A full calculation involves heat load/loss calculations, however a ready check method can be undertaken using psychrometric charts. Whichever method is adopted the Surveyor should be satisfied with the calculations.

.3 For the guidance of Surveyors the calculation using a psychrometric chart should be carried out as follows:

	Required Standard				
	Dry bulb °C per cent	humidity	Relative enthalpy kj/kg	Specific kg/kig (dry air)	Moisture control
Outside	32	78	93.5	0.0239	
Inside	29	50	62.0	0.0128	
Extraction rate			31.5	0.0111	

This can be used as a comparison for a proposed design, e.g.

Data given for proposed design

	Dry bulb °C	Wet bulb °C	Relative humidity per cent
Outside	33	28	–
Inside	28	–	50

Therefore from the psychrometric chart:

	Dry bulb °C	Wet Bulb °C	Relative humidity per cent	Specific enthalpy kj/kg	Moisture control kg/kg (dry air)
Outside	33	28	–	89.5	0.022
Inside	28	–	50	59.2	0.012
Extraction rate				30.3	0.010

For acceptance on the basis of the above data the total heat drop and moisture content extraction are to be at least equal to the standard design. The above calculation indicates that the proposed design performance may fall below the required standard. In such a case, unless detailed heat-load calculations demonstrate that the required standard is met, the proposed design performance should not be accepted.

2.12.4.3 Control System
Adequate controls should be provided to enable comfortable conditions to be maintained within the accommodation when the less onerous ambient conditions prevail and also where the capacity of the plant exceeds the minimum requirements specified in sub-paragraph (b).

2.12.4.4 Thermal Insulation
The capacity of the air-conditioning plant and the performance of the plant will be affected by the provision of thermal insulation or lack of such insulation provided to the external boundaries of the crew accommodation and to heat producing spaces within the confines of the crew accommodation. Hence the builder or sub-contractor responsible for the design of the system should confirm that his proposed design specification takes into account the thermal insulation proposed for the ship.

2.12.4.5 Number of Conditioned Air Changes
.1 The number of changes of conditioned air in each compartment or space should be calculated having regard to the heat transfer into the space via the boundaries but in no case should the changes be less than those required by the Regulations.

.2 When air changes approaching this minimum are specified the system should be carefully balanced on completion to ensure that the air changes in each individual space do not fall below those quoted.

2.12.4.6 Recirculation of Supply Air
.1 Recirculation of supply air may be permitted provided that sanitary accommodation is provided with mechanical exhaust ventilation and that the fresh air content of the supply to the accommodation is not less than:
.1.1 25 cubic metres per hour for each person for whom accommodation is provided,
or
.1.2 the total capacity of the sanitary and any other accommodation exhaust fans, excluding the galley,

whichever is the greater.

.2 Additional natural exhaust with damper controls should be provided in order that the system can be balanced when recirculation is not in operation. Particular care should be exercised in the siting of the inlets to the recirculation systems. The grilles are to extract only from accommodation passageways and should be fitted on more than one tier of the accommodation, if practicable. They should be sited in positions which are not adjacent to a doorway to a galley, laundry, sanitary accommodation or to a similar space. In such cases it is unnecessary to have a direct supply to these passageways.

.3 Care should be taken to ensure that noise originating from the air-conditioning plant is not transmitted to the accommodation via recirculation inlets which are unduly large or sited in close proximity to the fan room.

.4 Notwithstanding the above it may be necessary in certain ambient conditions when tankers, gas carriers and chemical carriers are loading or discharging cargo for all air intakes and exhaust outlets to be closed and the air conditioning system to be operated on 100 per cent recirculation, for safety reasons. This may be accepted and the system designed accordingly provided the following is carried out:

    4.1 that 100 per cent recirculation will only be employed during loading or discharging cargo and at no other time. Accordingly, where Surveyors know that systems are being designed for this purpose they are to inform Owners in writing of the above, so that the Owners can in turn inform their masters,

    .4.2 that the ventilation system to cabins and messrooms is by air-conditioned supply with natural exhaust from these spaces to adjacent passageways,

    .4.3 that a CO_2 monitoring device is fitted with audible and visible alarms in each recirculation trunk. The monitoring device is to be so calibrated that it will be activated when the CO_2 content reaches 1,200 ppm by volume,

    .4.4 that the master is informed by standing instructions that if and when the alarms are activated loading or discharging of cargo is to be discontinued and that when it is safe to do so the accommodation spaces should be thoroughly ventilated with fresh air before recirculation is recommenced,

    .4.5 that monitoring devices are kept in full working order and regularly maintained.

Note: Provided the CO_2 content of the recirculated air-conditioned air does not exceed 1,200 ppm by volume it is considered on the basis of medical advice that the CO_2 will not have any adverse effect on personnel.

2.12.4.7 MECHANICAL EXHAUST

.1 When mechanical exhaust is provided for washing and sanitary accommodation, laundries, drying rooms, pantries and changing rooms, the exhaust system is to provide air changes not less than:

    .1.1 10 per hour for private bathrooms;

    .1.2 15 per hour for other spaces;

    .1.3 25 per cent in excess of any mechanical air supply which may be fitted for heating or any other purpose.

.2 Where a water closet compartment opens directly from an accommodation passageway the door is to be self-closing and close-fitting without apertures unless the mechanical exhaust ventilation provides for 30 changes of air per hour.

2.12.4.8 DOORS, SIDESCUTTLES, WINDOWS ETC

To ensure that the air-conditioning plant will maintain its designed performance doors leading from the accommodation to the open deck should be of the self closing type. Notices should be displayed in prominent positions in passageways to the effect that the ship is provided with an air-conditioning system and when this system is in operation sidescuttles, windows and skylights should be kept closed.

2.12.4.9 AIR TERMINALS
Air terminals in sleeping rooms and messrooms may be of the grille, diffusing louvre, ceiling diffusion or other acceptable pattern. They are to be sited so as to minimise noise, ensure uniform distribution throughout the space and avoid short circuiting to the exhaust.

2.12.4.10 TRANSFER OPENINGS
A correct balance between the supply and exhaust is to be achieved in each space by the provision of suitable transfer openings. Sufficient area can normally be achieved in these cases by allowing an opening not exceeding 25 millimetres under the doors to each room. If in extreme cases it is necessary to supplement this area, louvres with sliding shutters may be permitted in the lower portion of the door, subject to the requirement of the relevant Fire Protection Regulations.

2.12.4.11 NON-RETURN VALVE
A non-return valve is to be fitted in the air-conditioning supply to the hospital and associated spaces. Non-return flaps should also be fitted as necessary to supply and exhaust systems to any other spaces where there is a risk of effluvia passing to the living spaces when fans are stopped.

2.12.4.12 REFRIGERATION MACHINERY
All air-conditioning systems should have their refrigeration machinery independent of cargo plant. The refrigeration machinery should be designed with sea water for condenser cooling purposes at a minimum temperature of 32°C. The fouling factor of the condensers could be taken at 0.001.

It should not be possible for any toxic gas to pass, by leakage or otherwise, into the supply air stream.

2.12.4.14 SPARE GEAR
Spare gear should be provided for each ship in accordance with Schedule 4 to the Regulations, due consideration being given to the type of machinery fitted.

2.12.5 *Electric Table Fans*
See Regulation 35(9) noting that in ships provided with natural ventilation it is also recommended that consideration be given to providing electric table fans in all accommodation space to ensure good air movement under all ambient conditions. The fans should:

.1 be quiet in operation and fixed in position on 'semi-rigid' mountings.

.2 In a mess room or a galley, be provided with an oscillating mechanism which will operate automatically and rotate the axis through an angle of 90; otherwise additional fans should be fitted.

.3 be provided with speed regulators capable of providing at least two running speeds.

.4 have the mounting, blades and guards (if necessary) of rust proof construction.

.5 be fitted so as to prevent interference with the ship's radio, compasses, or any other navigational aid.

2.12.6 *Testing on Completion*

.1 In ships provided with a trunked mechanical ventilation system or an air conditioning system tests should be carried out on completion by the builder or contractor to demonstrate to the Surveyor that the requirements of the Regulations are being met.

.2 It is only necessary to take readings in selected spaces but before these are taken all louvres etc in all spaces should be opened. All spaces should be checked even if readings are not recorded.

.3 In a ship in which the trunked mechanical ventilation system supplies warm air for heating purposes, heating may be by-passed for tests under ambient conditions.

.4 The apparatus and methods used for the purpose of measuring air volumes should be certified correct with a tolerance of 3 per cent. The certificate should be issued by a recognised authority.

.5 Tests results should be prepared by the builder or contractor and should show in respect of the various spaces tested the designed air changes per hour and the corresponding air changes per hour achieved under test. See also para 2.12.4.2.

2.13 Sidescuttles and Windows

2.13.1 See Regulation 17 noting that its requirements may be overridden by the requirements of other Merchant Shipping Regulations, directly relating to safety, for particular arrangements and ship types and that:

.1 Sidescuttles and windows should comply with the relevant Fire Protection Regulations and The Merchant Shipping (Load Line) Rules 1968.

.2 Where an owner requires, for additional safety, all sidescuttles and windows in the types of ships referred to above to be of the non-opening type the Department will accept the arrangement provided the following applies:

    .2.1 the ship is air-conditioned and two air-conditioning units are fitted onboard which are cross connected by ducting so that in the event of one of the units failing the other unit will supply air for all the accommodation at reduced air changes.

    .2.2 in addition to the Regulatory spares a spare motor is supplied for the air-conditioning unit so that any loss of air supply would be for a short period only.

    .2.3 the mechanical exhaust system from private or semi-private toilets is operated separately, thus ensuring further movement of air,

    .2.4 the owner provides a written assurance that the air-conditioning system will always be available when the crew are onboard.

2.14 Drainage

2.14.1 See Regulation 18 noting that:

.1 When liable to flooding in heavy weather, floors should be drained by one of the following means:

1.1 overboard through a grating in the floor with a storm valve at the ship's side, or

1.2 to a pump suction, or

1.3 from deckhouses to the open deck with captive screwed caps or plugs.

.2 The floors of wash places, bathrooms and water closet compartments, unless draining to a pump suction, should be provided with scuppers having gratings in the lowest part at floor level and storm valves at the ship's side if led directly overboard, except that in the case of a private bathroom provided solely for the use of one person scuppers need not be fitted.

.3 Scuppers draining external open decks should not be combined with those provided within accommodation spaces.

.4 The internal drainage arrangements should be so designed as to minimise effluvia in the accommodation, whether by siphonage or by blow back. Hence drains from washbasins, baths, shower trays and sinks should be trapped with water seals of at least 75 millimetres and provided with storm valves at the ship's side if led directly overboard.

.5 Main drains which are employed to collect discharges from numerous fittings should be ventilated to the open air by one or more pipes. One such pipe should be situated above any storm valve fitted and if the main drain is extensive in length another pipe should be provided at the extremity of the drain. The area of the pipe or the combined area of the pipes, as the case may be, should not be less than the area of the main drain.

.6 Piping used for drainage purposes should, as far as is practicable, be carried well clear of the deck to facilitate cleaning. Clearing plugs or caps should be provided at traps and elsewhere as necessary, and the pipes should, wherever practicable, have a good fall.

.7 Due regard should be paid to the avoidance of sharp bends or knees and to varying inclinations of the ship.

.8 Where a collecting tank or a sewage treatment plant into which drains pass is installed scuppers should be trapped with water seals of at least 75 millimetres. Suitable alternative arrangements should be made for waste disposal in the event of failure of pumps provided for emptying the collecting tank or sewage treatment plant.

.9 The arrangement of a common one pipe waste line for drainage from washbasins, sinks, showers, scuppers and WCs may be accepted provided that each individual drainage pipe is fitted with an anti-siphonic vent so arranged as to eliminate the risk of seal breakage from induced syphonage, back pressure or self-syphonage. Except where fitted with anti-siphonic arrangement's as above waste pipes should not share a discharge with soil pipes.

.10 Where it can be anticipated that contents of drainage from any space might be undesirable such systems shall be independent of other systems, e.g. galley, dry cleaning room.

With regard to the use of plastic piping for drain pipes and soil pipes see paragraph 2.8.5 of these Instructions.

2.15 Interior Finishes

2.15.1   See Regulation 19 noting that:

.1   Finishes are also subject to the relevant Fire Protection Regulations.

.2   It is recommended that for wall and ceilings light colours be used except where it is considered that the use of materials other than of light colours will in general improve the practicality and decor of the space. It should be noted that where surface finishes are other than light in colour additional lighting may be necessary to reach the standard required by the Regulations.

.3   Paints, including those having a metallic base, should not be applied on steel furniture, unless the surfaces have first been galvanised or rust-proofed. Painting will not be accepted as a substitute for such galvanising or rust-proofing.

2.16 Marking

2.16.1   See Regulation 20 noting that:

.1   On completion the markings required should be shown by the Surveyor on Form SUR 55 and forwarded to the builder or owner as the case may be.

.2   It is realised that in certain crew accommodation spaces with a highly decorative finish cutting in on the structure will not be appropriate. In these cases, the marking may either be cut in under the door lintel or if this is not possible 'label plates' may be affixed to the structure. If the latter are used they are to be attached in such a manner that they cannot readily be removed. If attached by screws, the slots in the screws should be removed after fixing, and when through bolts are used the ends should be clenched over.

.3   When the builder or owner has carried out the markings indicated on the Form SUR 55 the Surveyor should inspect each of the markings to ensure they are permanent and legible.

2.17 Sleeping Rooms

2.17.1   See Regulation 21 noting that:

.1   It is recommended that as far as practicable persons under the age of 18 should be berthed in sleeping rooms separate from those provided for other members of the crew.

.2   In deriving the floor area of sleeping rooms spaces occupied by berths, lockers, seats, chests of drawers and other furniture should be included in the area but spaces which by reason of their small size or irregular shape cannot accommodate furniture and do not contribute to the area available for free movement should not be included. The space occupied by frame chocks and the space between frame brackets if it is not covered or occupied by fixed furniture and is not available for free movement should not be included in the area. If the sides tumble home, a vertical line which meets the side at a height of 1.98 metres above the floor is to be the outer boundary of the measurements, the 'side' being either the framing, lining or other structural material as the case may be.

.3 The radio officer's sleeping room should be sufficiently near the radio room for the radio officer to reach his post in 30 seconds. In calculating this figure, an unobstructed route of 46 metres should be regarded as equivalent to 30 seconds travelling time between the two points. 'Unobstructed' should be interpreted as referring to a route which is accessible at all times when the ship is at sea. When measuring the route, vertical distances at ladders should be multiplied by 3.

.4 Wherever practicable a day room, adjoining their sleeping room, shall be provided for officers.

2.18 Beds

2.18.1   See Regulation 22 noting that:

.1 Where avoidable, beds should not be placed below pipes carrying water particularly soil water being discharged from other accommodation (see also paragraph 2.8)

.2 It is a requirement that there should be unobstructed access to at least one side of each bed. In particular if the adjacent sides of two beds in the room are parallel to each other or, when projected, make an angle of less than 90° with each other, the distance between those sides at any point should not be less, wherever practicable, than 760 millimetres if the beds are in single tier and not less than 910 millimetres if they are in double tier.

.3 Where screens are required they should be fitted for the full length of the bed or the full width of the bed dependent upon whether the sides or ends abut and should extend from the bottom of the bed upwards for a height of at least 600 millimetres.

.4 With regard to the position of beds, they should be fitted
.4.1 Accepted 'good practice' is that beds should wherever practicable be positioned fore and aft.
.4.2 at least 100 millimetres clear of ventilation trunks, service piping and the like; and
.4.3 at least 50 millimetres clear of bulkheads or the ships side, unless so fitted as to facilitate the bedding being kept clean and dry while preventing the harbouring of dirt or vermin;
.4.4 with suitable air space around the mattress.

.5 When lee rails or leeboards are not fitted, the bulkheads in way of beds may be polished or alternatively, polished hardwood or plastic panels may be attached to the bulkheads in way of the bedding. Lee rails or leeboards on the side or sides which may be used for access or for sitting should not be higher than the top of the mattress, excepting at the head and foot.

.6 Consideration should be given to fitting wider beds where the size or service of the particular ship justifies.

.7 Mattresses should be of a proprietary make and in no case be less than 100 millimetres in thickness.

2.19 Furniture and Fittings in Sleeping Rooms

2.19.1   See Regulation 23 noting that:

.1   Additional equipment to that specified in the Regulations may be fitted provided that it does not interfere with the general comfort or reasonable free movement of the occupant or occupants as the case may be and facilitates tidiness.

.2   To facilitate cleaning and to prevent the harbouring of dirt and vermin furniture should either be arranged so that the base rests on the floor of the room or be provided with a space between the base and the floor, such space being not less than 150 millimetres.

.3   Furniture not built in, or fixed in such a way that vermin and dirt could be harboured should be moveable or should stand sufficiently far from bulkheads to enable cleaning and painting to be carried out as necessary.

.4   Chests of drawers placed below beds should be readily portable. Alternatively, a clear space of 50 millimetres should be left between drawers and bed to facilitate cleaning.

.5   The easy chair referred to in Regulation 23(5)(e)(ii) should be fully sprung and upholstered on the seat, back and arms; the seat should be low and not less than 525 millimetres deep and 500 millimetres wide; the back should be high enough and set at such an angle as to ensure comfort. There should be no crevices which cannot be readily cleaned and provision should be made for security in rough sea conditions. It may be found advantageous to arrange for the back of the chair to be detachable. A bed spread or cover should be provided for the bed if an easy chair is provided in lieu of a settee.

.6   Sidescuttle or window curtains should be such as to ensure a suitable standard of 'black out' when closed and be provided with means for securing them in the open position clear of the glass.

.7   The mirror and cabinet for toilet requisites may be combined for the purpose of compliance with the Regulations.

2.20   Mess Rooms

2.20.1   See Regulation 24 noting that:

.1   As far as the Department is concerned any one of the mess room arrangements allowed under the Regulations is acceptable and hence the choice of which scheme should be used is a matter for the builder and/or owner to decide.

.2   In determining the minimum total area of mess rooms the number of persons likely to use the room at any one time should be taken to be:
    .2.1   where no separate recreation room is provided the total complement entitled to use the mess room, or
    .2.2   where a separate recreation room is provided at least two-thirds of the total complement entitled to use the mess room.

.3   It is realised that in passenger ships in certain cases it will be impracticable to use the figures specified in (i) and (ii) above. In such a case and provided the owner is prepared to serve all meals at more than one sitting the number of persons likely to use the room at any one time may be taken to be:

.3.1 where no separate recreation room is provided at least one-half the total complement entitled to use the mess room, or

.3.2 where a separate recreation room is provided at least one-third the total complement entitled to use the mess room.

.4 In deriving the floor area of a mess room space occupied by tables, chairs, sideboards and other furniture should be included in the area but spaces which by reason of their small size or irregular shape cannot accommodate furniture and do not contribute to the area available for free movement should not be included. The space occupied by frame chocks and the space between frame brackets if it is not covered or occupied by fixed furniture and is not available for free movement should not be included in the area. If the sides tumble home, a vertical line which meets the side at a height of 1.98 metres above the floor is to be the outer boundary of the measurement, the 'side' being either the framing, lining or other structural material as the case may be.

.5 Duty mess rooms may be provided for officers and ratings subject to there being no reduction in area of the principal mess rooms required by the Regulation.

2.21 Furniture and Fittings in Mess Rooms

2.21.1 See Regulation 25 noting that:

.1 In determining the minimum number of seats required the number of persons likely to use the room at any one time should be taken to be the same as that outlined in paragraph 2.20.2.

.2 A hot press (or its equivalent) is to be an item of equipment designed to keep food that has already been cooked in a hot condition and ready for eating; it should not be capable of cooking food.

.3 No objection is raised to the provision of coffee making machines or apparatus, however means for boiling water for making tea should also be provided. Therefore hot water boilers should normally be fitted but in a ship with a small complement an electric kettle or kettles of suitable capacity are acceptable.

2.22 Recreation Spaces

2.22.1 See Regulation 26 noting that:

.1 Where the size or service of a ship or the number of crew justify, consideration should be given to providing recreation rooms separate from the mess.

.2 Where no separate recreation room is provided, it is recommended, that a separate portion of the mess room be set aside for recreational purposes and furnished with settees, easy chairs and occasional tables.

.3　Recreation or mess rooms should also incorporate suitable game playing facilities, unless these are provided in other agreed spaces.

.4　Although separate spaces for film and television facilities are preferable officers' and ratings' recreation or mess rooms may be used for this purpose.

2.23　Offices

2.23.1　See Regulation 27 noting that:

.1　The offices specified should not be combined with any other space and should be suitably equipped and furnished compatible with their function.

.2　Additional offices for the master, chief steward and seafarers' organisations representatives etc may also be provided.

.3　Offices should, wherever practicable, not be sited adjacent or near to sleeping rooms other than that of the user.

2.24　Sanitary accommodation

See Regulation 28 noting that:

2.24.1　*General*
.1　Normally wash basins will be made of vitreous china and baths of vitreous enamelled iron or coated pressed steel. However, no objection will be raised to the use of other materials, such as plastic, provided the material satisfies the requirements of the Regulations, the Surveyor is satisfied that they are sufficiently robust for their purpose and that relevant notices or advice are provided on board for the reference of the crew, detailing recommended cleaning methods.

.2　It is recommended that wash basins and baths be fitted with suitable overflow arrangements. The tap outlets should be at least 25 millimetres higher than the rim of wash basins or baths which are not fitted with overflow arrangements or 25 millimetres higher than the top of the overflow arrangements in the case of wash basins or baths fitted with such arrangements.

.3　Taps which provide other than fresh water should be labelled accordingly.

.4　In a space containing a fixed bath or shower there should be no socket or provision for the connection of portable electrical appliances except for low voltage (50 volts AC with a maximum voltage of 30 volts to earth or 50 volts DC) units. An exception to the above is a shower electrical supply socket complying with the relevant standards. In general all switches or other means of control or adjustment of electrical apparatus should be so situated as to be normally inaccessible to a person using a fixed bath or shower and should be of watertight construction.

2.24.2 *Baths*

.1 Should be at least 1.35 metres internal length except when fitted supplementary to a shower in which case they may be shorter.

.2 Should be rigidly fixed to prevent movement in a seaway and should not rely solely on fixation by the plumbing arrangements.

.3 Where baths are provided with showers the mixing valves for the showers should meet the requirements specified in paragraph 2.24.3 below. In such cases the Surveyor should ensure that the hot water being supplied to the bath is independent of the shower mixing valve so that the temperature of the hot water for the bath can comply with the requirement of the relevant Regulations.

2.24.3 *Showers*

.1 The floor area of showers should be at least 0.58 square metres and the sides should be suitably proportioned to allow easy access.

.2 Mixing valves which are not of the thermostatic type should be provided with arrangements such that the supply of hot and cold may be adjusted on completion so that the temperature requirement of the Regulations can be met. Such arrangements should not consist of taps and should be such that once set they cannot be readily tampered with by unauthorised persons. Hence adjustment controls should be concealed with covering devices.

.3 Shower spaces provided with mixing valves which are not of the thermostatic type should be provided with suitable warning notices advising users against the danger of scalding in the event of failure of the cold water supply.

.4 Mixing valves of the thermostatic type may be fitted provided that the type has first been approved by the Department. Manufacturers requiring approval of such valves should submit details see Annex 3.

.5 In approving thermostatic anti-scalding mixing valves the Department will require manufacturers to:
  5.1 Adjust each valve before its despatch from their works so that the maximum shower water temperature will not exceed 43°C, and
  5.2 Provide a copy of instructions for installing, operating and servicing for the retention and reference of the crew on board the ship.

.6 Screening to shower spaces for the purposes of dressing or undressing will be considered as being large enough provided the dimensions of the screened off space are of the order of 1.52 metres by 750 millimetres including the shower tray.

2.24.4 *Wash Basins*

.1 Should have a capacity of at least 7.0 litres measured to a level of about 38 millimetres below the rim of the bowl. Recognising the restrictions on available space in some vessels the capacity of wash basins may be reduced to not less than 4.5 litres where the larger size is impracticable.

.2 Should be spaced so as to afford adequate room for washing and, wherever practicable, in communal washplaces be spaced not less than approximately 750 millimetres apart centre to centre. If this is not practicable a smaller spacing may be adopted but the minimum which should be accepted is 550 millimetres. Single basins are preferable to a range but where two or more basins are combined in a single unit, arrangements should be provided to prevent water in one basin splashing over into another.

2.24.5 *Water Closets and Sewage Disposal*
2.24.5.1 WATER CLOSETS
.1 For the purpose of providing flush water, in all ships fitted with power driven bilge pumps, arrangements should be made for filling gravity 'sanitary' tanks by power through permanent connections, unless an enclosed pressure system or an adequate gravity supply is fitted. In other ships, hand pumps may be fitted. Suitable alternative pumping arrangements should be made in case the designated 'sanitary' pump breaks down.

.2 Service tanks should be fitted with suitable overflows. Their capacity should be commensurate with the size of the installation, and with the arrangements for replenishment.

.3 Enclosed pressure systems should have automatic controls for the pumps. The reservoir should be of a capacity adequate for peak demands.

.4 Ships intended for service in very cold climates should have suitable protection against freezing up.

.5 In view of the uses to which sea water is put onboard ships, such as for making fresh water from fresh water generators and/or reverse osmosis plants, sanitary discharges should be situated aft of and on the opposite side of the ship to such sea inlets. In any case, they should be sited well below, and as far as possible from, any sea inlet.

.6 Service pipes from any salt water service tanks or pressure systems should be independent of the wash deck or fire mains but small draw off taps may be provided in the service pipes for washing down floors of washplaces and water closets.

.7 Water closet pedestals and flushing arrangements should be so designed as to ensure the complete clearance of the bowl and trap. On completion this should be demonstrated to the satisfaction of the Surveyor.

.8 Where fresh water, whether drinking and/or washing, is to be used for flushing water closets arrangements should be made to prevent possible contamination of the water by back-siphonage. Typical arrangements that may be accepted for this purpose, are as follows:
　.1 A vacuum breaker should be fitted between the flushing valve and the water closet pan at least 100 millimetres above the rim of the pan, or
　.2 A suitable type of cistern should be provided.

.9 When considering 2.24.5.1.8.2 the Surveyor in examining the cisterns should take the following into account:
　.9.1 It should be of robust construction such that it is suitable for use on ships,
　.9.2 No silencer tube should be fitted but arrangements should be made to diffuse the water entering the cistern,
　.9.3 The normal water level should be at least 50 millimetres below the point of entry of the water,

.9.4 The overflow should be so positioned within the cistern that if the cistern should fill with water without the cut-off valve operating it would discharge over the weir of the siphon and flow into the water closet pan. Overflow should occur when the water level is approximately halfway between the normal water level and the point of entry,

.9.5 The cistern should be adequately ventilated in order not to impede rapid discharge when flushing,

.9.6 The lid should be adequately secured and sealed,

.9.7 The aperture for the operating handle should be watertight against the surging of the water,

.9.8 It should operate satisfactorily with the ship having a list of 15° in either direction with the water level at all times below the inlet.

2.24.5.2 SEWAGE DISPOSAL

.1 Annex IV of the International Convention for the Prevention of Pollution from Ships 1973 as amended by the Protocol of 1978 to that Convention (MARPOL 73/78) contains regulations for the prevention of pollution by sewage from ships. At the time of printing these instructions, Annex IV was not in force but had been ratified by some 28 member states with 41.54% of the gross tonnage of the world's merchant shipping.

.2 When the Annex enters into force every new United Kingdom ship and 10 years thereafter every existing United Kingdom ship subject to the provisions of Annex IV will require to be fitted with one of the following sewage systems:

.2.1 A sewage treatment plant of a type approved by the Department, based on the standards and test methods developed by the International maritime Organisation (IMO) or

.2.2 A sewage, collecting and disinfecting system of a type approved by the Department based on the standards and test methods developed by the IMO. Such a system shall be fitted with facilities, to the satisfaction of the Department, for the temporary storage of sewage when the ship is less than 4 nautical miles from the nearest land or

.2.3 A holding tank of a capacity to the satisfaction of the Department for the retention of all sewage, having regard to the operation of the ship, the number of persons on board and other relevant factors. The holding tank shall be constructed to the satisfaction of the Department and shall have a means to indicate visually the amount of its contents.

.3 There are as yet no specific UK requirements for sewage treatment systems however the Department has given type approval and issued a certificate of type test to a number of sewage treatment plants on the basis of recommendations on international effluent standards and guidelines for performance tests for sewage treatment plants laid down by the IMO. Ships fitted with these treatment plants should have little difficulty in meeting the standards of Annex IV when it enters into force.

.4 Guidelines for the approval of holding tanks or comminuting and disinfecting systems have yet to be developed at IMO.

.5 Where it is proposed to install a sewage plant which uses treated effluent for flushing water closets or is designed with novel features, details should be obtained for consideration prior to installation.

.6 Sewage tanks, whether they be of the collecting type only or combine collection with treatment, should be sited as far as practicable from fresh water tanks. In no circumstances should they be located above a fresh water tank even though a cofferdam is provided.

.7 Where a sewage tank is sited in the same compartment as a fresh water tank as sometimes unavoidably happens in the case of passenger ships the longitudinal separation should be as great as practicable. Where the tanks are sited in close proximity to each other a cofferdam should be provided between them. To prevent possibility of contamination in such a case the access to the fresh water tank should not be in the same compartment as the access to the sewage tank. If this cannot be achieved by suitable siting of access manholes, a trunked watertight access or similar should be provided leading to the fresh water tank.

.8 Where water closets are not connected to an approved vacuum discharge pipe system the soil pipes diameter should be taken as the bore of the pipe which should be maintained throughout the length of the pipe except that when main drains are employed the bore of the main drains should be suitably increased in zones commensurate with providing efficient and effective drainage. Soil pipes should have a continuous fall to the discharge. Alternatively, other arrangements should be provided to ensure that the water closet will function effectively, even if the ship has a list or train of 10°. They should be suitably ventilated to prevent blow backs in the accommodation see also paragraph 2.14 above.

2.24.5.3 TESTING

On completion the Surveyor should test hot and cold water supplies to wash basins, baths and showers and in particular be satisfied that the temperature requirements of the Regulations can be met. Water closets and the sewage disposal system should also be tested to ensure that they function correctly and in accordance with any relevant conditions of approval, for example vacuum sewage system are type approved.

2.25 Supply of drinking and fresh water

See Regulations 29 and 30 noting that:

2.25.1 *General*

Distinctions between the drinking and fresh washing water with reference to the water quality desired, having regard to all types of dangerous water borne bacteria, are now non-existent. Most dangerous bacteria in water affecting humans are ingested in drinking water but, significantly, legionella bacteria can gain entry to the respiratory system from water suspended in air in the form of a fine mist created by shower, tap sprays etc. Whenever possible the fresh water systems should be independent of any other services, for example engine room systems, and it is important that the design, construction and materials used facilitate cleaning and minimise the risks of contamination.

2.25.2 *Fittings and Accessories*

All fittings and accessories used in the construction of ships' freshwater plumbing systems should be of a type which do not bleach out toxic constituents or provide a habitat for bacteria, which can occur in the case of natural rubber, various plastics, and fibre accessories. It is required therefore in line with the policy adopted by all shore side Water Authorities in the United Kingdom (under the United Kingdom Water Fittings Byelaws Scheme), that all materials used in freshwater systems should be attested and listed in the current edition of the Water Fittings and Materials Directory (revised annually) prepared by the Water Research Centre, Henley Road, Medmenham, PO Box 16, Marlow, Bucks SL7 2HD, i.e. pumps, valves, 'o' rings, seatings, compounds, pipes, shower mixers, taps, calorifiers and all other sundry items. When a vessel is constructed or refitted abroad fittings or materials validated by a local material agency to an equivalent standard may be acceptable given suitable documentary attestation is available.

2.25.3 *Storage Tanks*
2.25.3.1 CAPACITY
.5 A suitable capacity for fresh water storage tanks can be calculated as follows:
  - .5.1 for drinking water allow not less than 18 litres for each member of the crew for each day likely to elapse between successive replenishments of water, and
  - .5.2 similarly for washing water allow not less than 72 litres per day between replenishments for each member of the crew, or
  - .5.3 noting the common standard of fresh water required for domestic purposes, see para 2.25.1 above, tanks for drinking and washing water may be combined to produce a capacity of 90 litres per person per day.

.6 Where plant producing fresh water is provided on board (see Annex 1) so allowing the storage capacity to be reduced the capacity is still required to be justified with reference to the number of plant(s) fitted and the maximum length of sea voyage anticipated.

2.25.3.2 SITING
.1 Tanks intended for domestic fresh water should normally be sited above the inner bottom and independent of the hull but tanks other than peak tanks (which are difficult to clean) not independent of the hull may be utilised if they are of all welded construction and suitable in all other respects. All fresh water tanks should be so sited and be of such dimensions that they are readily accessible to facilitate inspection, cleaning and coating.

.2 Where it is necessary to use double bottom tanks they should not be less than 900 millimetres depth and be arranged to facilitate inspection, cleaning and coating. In ships with only one fresh water storage tank sited in the double bottom an alternative reserve drinking water tank should be provided for use in an emergency.

.3 In ships of less than 2,500 gross tons where the use of an aft peak tank cannot be avoided particular attention should be given to filling and smoothing the bottom recesses in the tank with cement or other suitable non-toxic composition. Fore peak tanks, which are suscep-tible to damage and contamination should not be used.

.4 WCs, laundries or any other facilities likely to contaminate fresh water should be positioned clear of the crown of fresh water tanks.

.5 No domestic fresh water tank should have a common boundary with any tank used for other than fresh or salt clean water ballast.

.6 Manhole accesses should be of adequate size, sited clear of possible sources of contamination and where sited in tank crowns should be fitted with raised coamings.

2.25.3.3 Construction

.1 The internal structure of all fresh water tanks should be designed to ensure efficient drainage through adequate limber holes to the suction and continuous welding should be used.

.2 When new or on completion of repairs in an existing ship a pressure test of all freshwater tanks boundaries including the outer shell of the ship where this applies should be conducted to ensure that there is no seepage into the fresh water tanks from the sea or adjacent water ballast tanks.

.3 No piping other than piping containing fresh water of the same standard should pass through a fresh water tank.

.4 Air, filling and where practicable sounding pipes, should stand sufficiently high above the deck or tank crown to prevent fouling. Air pipes should be of the swan neck type fitted with a wire guage and should be sited in a protected position where the entry of sea water on deck is prevented.

.5 Sight glasses or gauges should be provided where practicable to indicate the water level in the storage tanks in order to avoid as far as possible the use of sounding rods.

2.25.3.4 Coatings

Freshwater tank steel structure when new should be thoroughly wire brushed, scrubbed and primed before coating with cement wash or a proprietary coating system and should be thoroughly aired and dried before filling. When coating systems other than cement wash are used such as epoxy finishes specially developed for fresh water tanks it is essential that the coatings are applied and allowed to cure strictly in accordance with the manufacturers instructions otherwise the water can subsequently become unfit for use. The manufacturer's advice on filling, flushing and employing fresh water tanks before they are connected to the distribution system should be closely adhered to.

2.25.3.4 Filling Arrangements

.1 Fresh water obtained from shore mains or water barge should be transferred by a hose exclusively used for that purpose. Hoses where carried on board ships should be suitably marked and should be provided with closing caps at each end and should be stowed in a position clear of the deck where they are not subject to contamination.

.2 Fresh water producing plants such as low pressure generators or reverse osmosis plants shall be of an approved type all in accordance with Annex 1.

2.25.4 *Disinfection of Domestic Water Systems*

.1 Where fresh water producing plant is fitted this is commonly achieved by the installation of an automatic chlorination unit in the delivery line between the plant and the storage tank(s). Another accepted means is an approved silver ions discharge unit similarly fitted, see Annex 1.

.2 It should be particularly noted that since June 1986 ultra violet sterilizer units alone are no longer acceptable in lieu of an automatic means of sterilization involving chemical treatment as described above although they are accepted and recommended as a supplementary treatment system.

.3 Shore mains water in the United Kingdom normally contains only a very low concentration of free chlorine and the ship environment decreases this further. In foreign countries there may be no free chlorine content at all. All fresh water taken from shore or water barge should therefore be chlorinated on loading. Chlorination may be achieved by the traditional manual method using the revised formulae given in the Ship Captain's Medical Guide or by using an automatic chlorination unit in the ship's deck filling line.

.4 .4.2 Disinfection of shipboard domestic water, and the associated system, using chlorine, should be such that a residual free chlorine concentration at all outlets of 0.2 ppm is achieved. The concentration may be checked by means of a Lovibond comparator kit.

.4.3 Where other means of disinfection are proposed the procedures are to be approved by the Department.

2.25.5 *Distribution System*
2.25.5.1 GENERAL
.1 Unless a gravity supply direct from the storage tanks can be obtained at the draw-off points, distribution of water should be achieved by pumps reserved for that purpose. Such pumps should have permanent connections to the service tanks, which should be fitted with overflows led back to the storage tanks.

.2 Where service tanks are fitted they should be of a size sufficient to meet peak demands and adequate for the capacity and method of operating the pumps.

.3 Alternative pumping arrangements should be made in the event of a breakdown of a power pump and such reserve pump may, in smaller systems be a self-priming hand operating pump.

.4 Where an enclosed pressure system is employed, suitable arrangements should be made for pumping by power in the event of breakdown. The reservoirs or pressure tanks should be of a size adequate for peak demands.

.5 Where compressed air supply is fitted to a reservoir or pressure tank the air supply line should be entirely separate from that provided for any other purpose and a screw down non-return valve should be arranged in the line.

.6 A non-return valve should be fitted in the delivery line from the pressure tank to the hot fresh water system where this service is shared.

2.25.5.2 CALORIFIERS
.1 These should be designed to avoid stagnant zones forming and should be fitted with efficient connections at the lowest point of the unit to ensure that all loose scale, or sludge can be completely drained off after cleaning and maintenance. In addition adequate access should be provided to enable scale deposits or products of corrosion to be removed and cleaning to be facilitated.

.2 Should be so sited as to minimise discomfort to the crew. Calorifiers and boilers should either be vented to the open air or provided with a safety valve adjusted to suit the working pressure except that ships operating in cold climates where the water might freeze if a vent pipe was fitted should be provided with a safety valve or equivalent means for limiting pressure.

.3 Where heating of water is effected by exhaust gas from engines which will not or may not be in use in port, suitable alternative arrangements should be made to ensure that when in port, the supply of hot fresh water can be maintained. Where hot water is supplied in association with a central heating plant, the water for washing purposes should be drawn from an individual cylinder, or calorifier, and the size of the heating boiler should be suitably increased.

2.25.5.3 PIPING

.1 Hot and cold water pipes should be kept sufficiently separated or be adequately insulated to prevent transfer of heat from hot to cold lines. The distribution system should be designed to provide constant circulation of the systems and to avoid deadlegs.

.2 In ships with sleeping accommodation for more than 100 persons it is recommended that a pressure main system with circulation pumps be provided in both hot and cold water lines.

.3 Draw off taps which provide water for washing purposes which is not fresh water quality should be suitably labelled.

2.25.5.4 CORROSION AND SCALE INHIBITORS

It is often the practice to add scale or corrosion chemical inhibitors to the main or auxiliary diesel engine fresh jacket cooling water which is used as the heating medium in the ease of a low pressure flash generator. As there is a risk of leakage of such water into the flash distilled side of the evaporator it is required that such inhibitors are of a type approved by the Department, see Annex 1.

2.25.5.5 SEA SUCTIONS TO FRESH WATER PRODUCING PLANTS

.1 These should be sited forward and on the opposite side of the ship from any bilge or sanitary water discharges. Where this is impracticable they should be sited so that they are in a boundary flow stream in the ship's bottom well clear of that from dirty wastes outlets.

.2 The fresh water producing plant sea suction should not share an inlet well with sea suctions intended for any other purposes other than domestic services noting that chemical injection systems are sometimes installed in seawater inlet wells for machinery. Chemical injection systems are sometimes fitted in the sea inlet wells of main and auxiliary machinery to inhibit the growth of weed or muluscs which would otherwise tend to choke the inflow. Any chemicals proposed for such system must be approved by the Department, see Annex 1.

2.26 Facilities for washing and drying clothes and for hanging oilskins and working clothes

See Regulation 31 noting that:

2.26.1 Washing and Drying Arrangements

.1 Where practicable separate facilities for washing and drying clothes shall be provided for officers and ratings. If a communal laundry is provided a rota system should be implemented. Separate drying facilities for female members of the crew should be provided where practicable.

.2 In passenger ships where a laundry is provided principally for dealing with the ships linen this will not be accepted as meeting the requirement of the Regulation and laundry facilities for use by officers and ratings should be provided.

.3 Since in most ships laundry equipment will be available for use by every member of the crew, washing machines provided should be of the ordinary domestic type. Suitable instruction on the correct operation should be displayed adjacent to each machine.

.4 Drying machines of the type which dry clothes completely shall be of the heated tumbler drier type. Ordinary spin driers are not accepted as drying clothes completely.

.5 Washing and drying machines should be rigidly fixed in position so as to prevent movement in rough weather conditions and prevent movement due to their rotary action.

.6 No objection will be raised to the provision of rotary ironing machines provided that ordinary domestic type hand irons and ironing boards are provided in addition for the purpose of compliance with the Regulations.

.7 The heating arrangements in drying rooms shall be capable of being controlled independently of the heating of all other spaces in the ship. If electrical heaters are provided they should be of the 'black heat' type, being suitably sited and guarded to prevent clothes coming into contact with the heater.

2.26.2 Working clothes lockers

Oilskins and other working clothes should not be stored in the same compartment or locker and separate storage arrangements should be provided for each. It is preferable that individual lockers be provided and allocated to each member of the crew for these purposes but where lack of space prohibits this arrangement no objection will be raised to communal spaces provided these are separate for officers and ratings.

2.27 Galleys

See Regulation 32 noting that:—

2.27.1 General

.1 Where a galley is situated on an open deck consideration should be given to the provision of a horizontally divided weather door.

.2 If a skylight is provided it should in general be capable of being opened, but if there are grounds for objection to opening lights, fixed lights may be accepted provided there is adequate mechanical supply and exhaust ventilation and suitable natural ventilation. Opening flaps to skylights should be, accessible from inside the galley, provided with handy regulating devices and closeable from outside the galley.

.3 The provision of, ample supply ventilation including spot cooling as necessary and of openings for the outlet of moist warm air should be provided such that over-heating of local areas in the galley is minimised. If the natural ventilation is insufficient to provide sufficient air movement and no other steps are practicable mechanical exhaust ventilation should be fitted, even though the ship is not required by the Regulations to be provided with such ventilation, to ensure the rapid extraction of heat and fumes and the attainment of reasonable working conditions.

.4 Special care should be taken to ensure that electric lighting and supply fittings in the galley are adequate and suitable for their purpose.

2.27.2 *Equipment*

It is realised that the type of equipment, size and function will vary from ship to ship and that many owners will provide a greater variety of equipment and others will use alternative apparatus. Nevertheless the undermentioned equipment is a basis on which a galley should be equipped:

.1 A dresser of ample size with a hardwood top, drawers and an open front cupboard under which should be fitted portable shelves. One shelf for cook's condiments, etc over the dresser;

.2 A dresser with a stainless steel top having a sink of such dimensions as will allow the preparation of food and washing up of crockery and cooking utensils. The bottom of the sink should have rounded corners. Portable sparred shelves should be fitted under the dresser and a shelf or rack for washing-up liquids etc above. The waste pipe from the sink should be of adequate diameter and should lead through a sludge box on the galley floor. Where considered necessary a portable sludge strainer should be fitted over the drain in the sink;

.3 A baking board and a dough trough with filleted corners inside and hinged top made of hardwood or heavily tinned or rust-proof metal or glazed fireclay. A proving cupboard of capacity sufficient for the amount of bread required by the ship's complement except that in small ships where proving can adequately be carried out in front of the galley range a proving cupboard need not be provided;

.4 A hinged or portable serving table, if dresser space is inconveniently placed or insufficient for serving purposes;

.5 A seat, which may be hinged if necessary for better access;

.6 A small stool;

.7 A clock of the enclosed bulkhead type fixed to a bulkhead;

.8 Metal shelves with storm rails fitted at a convenient height above the deck over dressers;

.9 A steam or electrically heated drinking water boiler of adequate capacity fitted over the galley sink, with a lid, a gauge glass, a draw off tap and an overflow pipe led into the sink. The boiler should be mounted such that the adjacent areas can be readily kept clean.

.10 Drinking water should be led from the drinking water system to a position over the hot water boiler with a tap for filling. Spring-loaded, or where an owner requires, screw-down, hot fresh and cold drinking water non-concussive taps should be fitted over the sink. There should be an ample supply of fresh hot water for washing up purposes;

.11 An independent steamer of adequate size fitted with necessary trays. The use of a perforated steam coil supplied by steam direct from the ship's boiler or any other fitting using ordinary boiler steam which comes in contact with food is not permitted;

.12 A steel cupboard, full height if possible with portable shelves;

.13 Unless meat and similar stores are provided pre-prepared a heavy portable chopping and cutting board in addition to a chopping block near the refrigerated storeroom;

.14 Panracks of metal bars fitted close to the range but not above it;

.15 Adequate arrangements for heating plates. If a plate heating rack is fitted over the range it should be entirely enclosed. If there are more ovens than are required by the Regulations, an oven may be used for this purpose and no separate plate heating arrangements will be necessary.

.16 Where space does not permit the fitting of separate dressers outlined in .1 and .2 above they may be combined in one unit provided that the sink and surround are of stainless steel.

.17 The metal parts of the dressers and any cupboards clear of the wash-up sink and surround may be heavily galvanised.

.18 Where the bottoms of dressers and any cupboards are not flush with the deck a clearance of at least 300 millimetres should be provided in order to facilitate cleaning.

.19 Note: the equipment for baking is best kept in a separate compartment if space permits, otherwise it should be on one side of the galley to promote cleanliness.

2.27.3.1 GENERAL
Every galley shall be provided with one or more cooking appliances, usually fitted transversely, which subject to the following should include:

.1 in galleys intended to serve:
    .1.1 20 persons or less, one oven, or
    .1.2 more than 20 but not more than 60 persons, two ovens or
    .1.3 more than 60, three ovens

.2 an area of top-plate or boiling plate

2.27.3.2 CAPACITIES AND AREAS
The following figures are given for guidance:

.1 Oven(s) for combined roasting and baking in galleys intended to serve:
    .1.1 not more than 60 persons, 0.007 cubic metres per person
    .1.2 more than 60 persons, 0.0056 cubic metres per person subject to a minimum of 0.42 cubic metres and 0.022 square metres shelf area subject to a minimum of 1.8 square metres.

.2 For roasting only
   .2.1 When the total complement served by the galley is more than 60 but less than 121, 0.0028 cubic metres should be allowed for every member of the total complement, subject to a minimum of 0.21 cubic metres;
   .2.2 When the total complement served by the galley is more than 120 but less than 400 0.0023 cubic metres should be allowed for every member of the total complement;
   .2.3 When the total complement served by the galley is 400 or over, 0.0018 cubic metres should be allowed for every member of the total complement;

.3 Baking only: 0.015 square metres per person of shelf area but a smaller figure will be accepted in passenger ships if the staffing arrangements permit more than one baking a day; when separate provision is made for baking, a reasonable reduction will be allowed in the size of range top plates or boiling table provided there is independent boiling or steaming apparatus;

In cases where the crew do not generally eat food roasted or baked in ovens, the ranges provided for their use need not be fitted with ovens. The area of the top plate or boiling table should, however, be maintained.

2.27.3.3 NOTE
.1 The term 'top plate' and 'boiling table area' refers to the whole area of the top of the cooking appliances.

.2 The oven(s) and the boiling table may be separate appliances where this is desired.

.3 There should be ample clear space in front of the cooking appliance to provide a clear passage of at least 900 millimetres when the oven doors are fully open.

.4 Electric cooking appliances should have switches which will permit the amount of heat to be varied. The size and disposition of the heating elements should ensure that adequate heat is available on demand.

.5 Where an oil fired cooking appliance is provided special precautions may be necessary in connection with the heating arrangements in the fuel system. The fuel tank, filling, venting and the overflow from the fuel tank should be situated outside the galley and it should be possible to shut off the supply of fuel from the weather deck or other safe position outside the galley. Reference should also be made to the relevant Fire Protection Regulations.

.6 Where a cooking appliance is provided using liquefied petroleum gas as fuel the arrangements should comply with the requirements specified in the latest relevant standards.

2.27.4 Exceptions in those ships where the cooking facilities, if provided in accordance with above, would be inappropriate having regard to the distinctive national habits and customs of the crew there shall be provided agreed alternative facilities.

2.27.5 *Micro-Wave Ovens*
.1 May be provided and when fitted in galleys the Department may be prepared to vary the requirements in respect of cooking appliances. If fitted in pantries or messes there will be no reduction in the requirements with regard to the galley.

.2 Where micro-wave ovens are provided the following should apply:
   .2.1 they should comply with the latest relevant standards;
   .2.2 they should be suitable for the maximum ambient temperature which will be encountered in the spaces in which they are to be fitted;
   .2.3 they should be fitted with a thermal protective device arranged to interrupt the supply to the oven in the event of overheating, for example, should a timer failure occur;
   .2.4 a permanent notice should be displayed at each micro-wave oven to the effect that the machine must never be operated if the door interlock is inoperative, the door is damaged or ill fitting or the door seals are damaged;
   .2.5 they should be tested periodically for radiation leakage in service to ensure that the leakage levels do not exceed those allowed by the standards referred to in (i) above. Such tests should be carried out by a person having the necessary specialist knowledge and equipment.

2.28 Dry provision store rooms

See Regulation 33 noting that:

.1 Internal access to store rooms should be convenient to the galley. Shelves and other fittings should be so arranged as to avoid or minimise the lodgement of dust and vermin and to facilitate cleaning. Shelves should be of sparring of moderate width or of galvanised steel or other suitable material. Portable securing battens are preferable to fixed front ledges. The width of the shelves and the height between them should not be excessive so that all parts of the shelves are readily accessible.

.2 Racks should be large enough to take all the stores, leaving the floor clear for access and handling. Sufficient space for cleaning should be allowed between lower shelves or racks and the floor. Provisions should not be stowed against exposed steel bulkheads or ship's side.

.3 Circular galvanised removable bins with lids are preferable to fixed rectangular bins for cereals and they should be fitted conveniently for inspection and secured in place by removable bars.

.4 Where provision is made for hanging sides of bacon in the dry store room a rigid bar slotted or holed for hooks at intervals not exceeding 300 millimetres should be fitted.

.5 Stores which are likely to deteriorate, such as flour in bags, should be carried in either fixed racks set 300 millimetres above the floor or portable racks or gratings set 150 millimetres above the floor. In order to facilitate cleaning and inspection floor gratings should not be fitted. Where flour is carried in barrels there should be ample clearance from racks or shelves above so as to allow for easy storage and removal of barrels.

.6 Where access to a dry provision store room is by means of a hatch and stairway a lifting appliance should be fitted over the hatchway for storing the ship. Side boards which may be made to slip over the stairs should be fitted to minimise damage to stores by the stair treads when storing the ship.

.7 Precautions should be taken to prevent possible theft from store rooms by the provision of suitable padlocks for all solid and grating doors and hatch covers and by fitting closely spaced steel bars across the outside of sidescuttles and windows.

.8 Whenever practicable store rooms should be sited clear of heat producing spaces such as engine rooms, engine casings, boiler rooms and cargo or fuel oil tanks fitted with heating coils. Where this is not practicable the division between the store room and the heat producing space should be adequately insulated as follows:

.8.1 Floor
The steel deck forming the floor of the dry store room should be insulated with a suitable material and the top surface of the insulation provided with a suitable deck covering such that the combined insulation and covering will withstand the heavy usage associated with the transference of stores. Where the floor is situated over the propulsion machinery spaces the underside of the deck should be insulated with non-combustible material, and lined with galvanised sheet metal or other suitable non-combustible material. Where such linings have perforations, oil impervious membranes should be fitted on the face of the insulation. Where a store room adjoins the propulsion machinery spaces the upper side of the steel floor should be suitably insulated for a distance equal to approximately one beam space from the dividing bulkhead or casing.

.8.2 Boundary bulkheads
Where adjoining the propulsion machinery spaces, boundary bulkheads should be insulated with suitable non-combustible material on the dry store side and lined with plywood, hardwood or other suitable material on grounds. A pad of non-combustible insulation should be fitted between the grounds and the steel work of the bulkhead.

.8.3 Overhead deck
The overhead deck in a storeroom, where connected to propulsion machinery casing or bulkheads should be suitably insulated for a distance equal to approximately one beam space from the casing or bulkhead.

.8.4 Materials
Organic foam materials should not be used as insulating media in store rooms.

.9 Steam pipes should not pass through provision store rooms.

.10 Boundaries of dry provision store rooms exposed to the weather or sea in the case of a ship operating outside home trade limits or adjoining a refrigerated space in any ship should be suitably lined or insulated. The only exception to this might be where air conditioning is provided see sub-para n below.

.11 Where linings are provided they should be of suitable materials and the surface should be hard and without crevices. Seams and butts should be adequately and effectively sealed. Tongued and grooved wood should not be used for linings.

.12 The requirements for mechanical ventilation are given in Table II of Schedule 4 to the Regulations. Natural ventilation in vessels not provided with mechanical ventilation should provide an area of at least 6.83V square centimetres supply and the same exhaust, where, V is the volume of the store in cubic metres. At least one of the natural ventilators should have a cowl head and should be led down to near floor level. The exhaust ventilator should have local means of regulation and the air supply should be suitably diffused in order to avoid excessive drying of the stores exposed to a direct jet of air at a relatively high speed.

.13 Particular care should be taken to ensure that the ventilation of the store rooms is adequate but in the case of a bonded store the security necessary for customs purposes should not be impaired. For ratproofing of stores see paragraph 3.1.6 below.

.14 If storerooms are served from an air-conditioning system, agreed temperature and humidity control and monitoring will be required.

2.29 Cold store rooms and refrigerating equipment

See Regulation 34 noting that:

2.29.1 *General*
Each insulated room should have a separate electric light of robust construction with an outside switch and a pilot light. A watertight switch or push button should be fitted in each room, for use in the event of a person being inadvertently locked in the cold chambers it should be connected up to an alarm gong sited in the crew's living quarters so that it may attract immediate attention. The alarm gong should be suitably marked to show its purpose. The switches or buttons should be situated near the side of the doorways and should be distinguishable in the dark. In addition a red light outside the chamber should be included in the lighting circuit of the cold chambers with a watertight switch in the handing room controlling the circuit as well as the outside switch or switches. Means should be provided for releasing the door fastenings from the inside of every cold room.

2.29.2 *Alternative arrangements*
Deep freezers and refrigerators can be considered suitable for the purpose of providing 'adequate alternative cold storage arrangements; in such cases the following should apply:

.1 the size and number of deep freezers and refrigerators should be compatible with the period likely to elapse between successive replenishments of stores, and the number of crew, and shall be such that the risk of total loss of use is minimised;

.2 refrigerators should be used for the storage of ready use stores, butter, cheese, eggs etc;

.3 deep freezers and refrigerators should be suitably sited, where practicable for reasons of hygiene, in a separate compartment solely used for that purpose;

.4 all meat would require to be delivered to the ship as prepared joints and not in carcase form;

.5 all matters of detail such as ventilation, insulation having regard to the siting of the units, deck coverings, means of keeping the compartment clean, access and means of transporting food to the galley should be to the satisfaction of the Surveyor.

2.29.3 *Purpose-built rooms*

2.29.3.1 GENERAL

.1 Purpose-built cold store rooms will be regarded as adequate if they provide:

    .1.1 a meat room with a capacity of 0.17 cubic metres per man per month;

    .1.2 a vegetable room with a capacity of 0.113 cubic metres per man per month.

    .1.3 Whenever practicable a handling room should be provided; alternatively the capacity of the vegetable room should be increased to 0.14 cubic metres per man per month.

.2 The installation should be capable under marine conditions, with the machinery working not more than 12 hours a day of complying with the Regulations.

.3 Where grids are used for cooling they should be well distributed over the boundaries in order to promote economy in refrigeration and uniformity of temperature. Meat rooms should have grids overhead in addition to grids on the walls and should have thermostatic control so that the machine will cut in at the maximum permitted temperatures. If roof grids cannot be fitted in a meat room exceeding 10 cubic metres capacity, either

    .3.1 an air circulating fan should be installed to promote uniformity of temperature, or

    .3.2 the thermostat should be so positioned and set as to ensure that the maximum permitted temperature is not exceeded.

Failing the above, the thermostat should be set so that the machine will cut in at a temperature of at least 2°C less than the maximum permitted temperature.

.4 Proper arrangements should be made for hanging meat in the meat room, and for thawing it out after removal. A metal bar with hooks and a drip tray underneath is recommended. A chopping block of horizontal grained wood should be provided in a convenient position. If practicable shelves should be fitted in the handling room for 'ready use' purposes. If there is no handing room they should be fitted in the vegetable room or a thermostatically controlled refrigerated cupboard in the galley.

.5 Vegetable rooms exceeding 7 cubic metres capacity should preferably be air cooled by single bulkhead cooling battery and an ordinary 200 millimetre to 300 millimetre propeller type fan. A separate thermostat should be provided in the vegetable room.

2.29.3.2 INSULATION

.1 The boundary bulkheads, divisional bulkheads, floors and overhead decks of the cold rooms should be suitably insulated to maintain the temperatures specified in the Regulations.

Where adjacent spaces have a high fire risk rating, for example machinery spaces, the insulating medium should be of acceptable non-flammable material.

.2 Where it is proposed to use organic foam materials as the insulation medium cold store rooms should be located as far as practicable from other accommodation spaces and should be separated there-from by steel gastight bulkheads. Doors giving direct access from cold store room areas to other accommodation spaces should be of steel, gastight and self closing. Notices suitably positioned shall indicate 'POLYURETHANE FOAM. NO BURNING OR WELD-ING WITHOUT PERMISSION.' Bulkheads dividing other accommodation spaces or propulsion machinery spaces from cold store rooms should have fire insulation fitted on the accommodation or propulsion machinery boundaries to A60 standard. If the cold store rooms are sited over propulsion machinery spaces the underside of the deck should be insulated to A60 standard. The organic foam insulation should be covered within the cold store rooms by a non-combustible material e.g. stainless steel at least 1.0 millimetre thick or aluminium at least 1.6 millimetres thick.

2.29.3.3 CONSTRUCTION

.1 Grounds should be of timber 50 millimetres thick, bolted at 900 millimetres intervals to stiffeners, beams or lugs. Where no stiffeners are fitted the grounds should be spaced approximately 750 millimetres apart. Grounds for division bulkheads should be spaced 450 millimetres apart.

.2 The most satisfactory and hygienic lining is galvanised sheet steel or aluminium alloy but alternative materials may be fitted provided they have a hard face and are sufficiently robust to withstand usage associated with cold store rooms. Linings should be adequately secured to the grounds and if nails are used for this purpose they should be galvanised. Care should be taken to insulate linings from the ship's steelwork by fitting, where necessary, suitable insulation between the steelwork and the linings.

.3 The insulation on the floor of the cold store rooms should be covered with a suitable deck covering so that together with the materials used for the construction of the floor, they will withstand the heavy usage associated with the storage and transference of provisions.

.4 Strong battens or gratings of suitable material should be fitted over the whole of the floors. They should be of simple construction and if of whitewood be formed of 50 millimetre × 50 millimetre runners overlaid with 75 millimetre × 25 millimetre boards, in convenient portable sections, with a 25 millimetre gap between boards.

.5 Doors
  .5.1 Doors should preferably not be of the plug type but should have a full 3 millimetre clearance all round so as not to jam. They should rely for tightness on the facing action of a felt strip at least 6 millimetres thick, or preferably, a spongy round gasket about 13 millimetres in diameter secured round the outside edge of the top sides of the door and, in the case of meat and vegetable room doors, an additional strip or gasket secured to a rebate on the door frame, the doorway frame being rebated to suit. A large size gasket wiper should be fitted to the bottom of the door.
  .5.2 Should be as light in weight as possible to facilitate opening and closing. Devices should be provided so that when closed pressure may be exerted on the gaskets.
  .5.3 Where a handling room is provided the outside door to such a room should be quick acting and fitted with substantial slam type fasteners with wedge action.

50

.5.4 Hinges and other door fittings should be through fastened and doors should be capable of being opened from both sides.

.6 A 65 millimetre trapped scupper should, where practicable, be led from each cold room either overboard or into the bilge or a 50 millimetre drain fitted through the divisional bulkheads to permit free draining to a 65 millimetre scupper in the meat room. A small suction pump will be accepted as an alternative. Each scupper pipe should be fitted with a grating and a swivelled plate cover for closing. On the inside of the cold rooms a wood plug should be fitted to each drain tube.

.7 A dial type thermometer should where possible be placed in each room to indicate the temperature in a particular position (eg at the centre of the meat room). Alternatively, a thermometer tube with a screwed cap should be fitted in each room. A thermometer should be supplied for each tube together with 6 spare thermometers.

.8 White wood vertical sparring or dunnage battens, 50 millimetres × 50 millimetres, with chamfered outer edges, should be fitted approximately 370 millimetres apart on the bulkheads of the meat room clear of refrigeration pipes and shelving. Vertical battens, 25 millimetres × 25 millimetres, should be fitted approximately 370 millimetres apart from floor to ceiling in the vegetable room on the inside linings of the boundary bulkheads.

.9 Shelving and battens should be varnished before erection.

2.30 Hospitals

See Regulation 35 noting that:

.1 In passenger ships provided with a hospital complex which includes wards for passengers, separate wards for crew as specified in Regulation 35(23), an operating theatre, consulting rooms, bathrooms etc it is recommended that when the siting, design, layout, fitting, fixtures and services are being considered by owners and/or builders the services of a consultant medical practitioner be used.

.2 Where (.1) above applies special pantry facilities including a hot water boiler, domestic refrigerator, dresser, sink and cold drinking water should be provided for the hospital. Alternatively, the hospital should be so sited that the serving of hot food and drink can be conveniently arranged.

.3 The interior finish of the bulkheads of the hospital ward should be light and restful in colour.

.4 The portable electric lamp required by the Regulations should be provided with such accessories as are necessary for its practical use.

.5 In ships in which the Regulations do not require a permanent hospital but require the provision of a temporary hospital the owner's or pilot's room, if any, can be considered for use as a temporary hospital if required. If a spare room can be provided only by reducing the size of the crew accommodation, arrangements might be made for one sleeping room to be fitted with a spare bed to be used in an emergency by the occupant of a single berth room which would then be used as a temporary hospital.

2.31 Medical Cabinet

See Regulation 36 noting that:

.1 A suitably equipped dispensary will be acceptable in place of the medical cabinet required by the Regulations.

.2 In no circumstances should the medical cabinet be sited in the hospital ward(s). It should be sited in a passageway adjacent to the hospital or other suitable place.

.3 The Merchant Shipping (Medical Scales) Regulations require a copy of The Ship Captain's Medical Guide to be carried in every ship. Unless a ship has a duly qualified doctor or qualified nurse on board or the medical cabinet is under the supervision of the master it is recommended that the Medical Guide be carried in the medical cabinet and provision should therefore be made for its storage.

.4 Ventilation of the medical cabinet will be considered as being suitable if holes (1 cm diameter) protected by fine gauze are provided in the top of the outer door.

2.32 Protection from mosquitoes

2.32.1 See Regulation 37 noting that:

.1 Screens, when fitted, should fit tightly and be provided with a positive means of security. In the case of sidescuttle openings the foregoing requirements would be satisfied by fitting metal lugs on the edge of the screen frame to engage with the toggle bolts which are provided for securing the glass holder, together with a light clip at the appropriate point to fit behind the hinge of the glass part. The clip can be used for hanging the screen adjacent to the side scuttle when not in use. The screen frame should be rebated so that the full clamping effect of the bolts can be obtained and it should fit snugly on the ridge around the inside edge of the side scuttle rim.

.2 All natural ventilators should have either a framed shutter, hinged or sliding, of suitable gauze, positively secured in place, or a box fastened to the underside of the deck with gauze sides and a trap door at the bottom for cleaning purposes.

.3 The area of the screen should be large enough to compensate for the ventilation area lost on account of the wire mesh of the protective gauze. The arrangement in addition to allowing for cleaning the gauze should permit the full area of the ventilator to be available when the gauze is not required.

.4 Screen doors or panels should be fitted to the doorways of all doors to crew accommodation spaces, unless they are fitted to the doorways of the passageways leading to the open air.

.5 Screened doors fitted in passageways leading to the open air should be self closing.

.6 Where metal screens are used, the metal should be copper, bronze or monel metal, the last two being more resistant to sea atmosphere than copper. Wire of either 28 SWG (0.375 millimetres diameter) or 30 SWG (0.314 millimetres diameter) is recommended and the apertures of the gauze should be 1.219 millimetres, this combination giving approximately 6 apertures to the centimetre.

CHAPTER 3

Miscellaneous

3.1 Rodent and Vermin Control

The standard reference is 'Guide to Ship Sanitation' published by the
World Health Organisation (WHO).

3.1.1 *General*
Rodents in a vessel are a menace to health and uneconomic. It is therefore
important that every endeavour should be made to render their existence
as difficult as possible.

They are very prolific in their breeding habits and their numbers increase
daily. They dislike open spaces and thrive in dark corners or secluded
spaces which are not easily accessible. If therefore during the construction
of the crew accommodation potential nesting spaces and runs can be
eliminated this will go a long way towards keeping a ship rodent free
and will reduce the cost and delay of periodic fumigation. It is important
to realise that a small rodent can pass through small holes, they will not
gnaw a flat surface but will generally attack corners and edges of timber.
Any gratings or wire mesh used to close off spaces should have apertures
no larger than 9 millimetres.

It is appreciated that in the construction of crew accommodation it is
sometimes difficult to avoid corners or pockets but by exercising care
much can be done to minimise the conditions favourable to harbouring
and nesting and hence make the life of a rodent as difficult as possible.

3.1.2 *Bulkheads*
Each compartment or group of compartments should, as far as possible
be isolated as a rodent proof space by effectively closing all openings
into adjacent compartments; by this means runs will be avoided. All
necessary openings such as ventilation ducts should be screened at the
bulkhead if no mesh is fitted at the apertures.

If bulkheads or partitions with ventilation openings at the top form the
boundaries of a compartment or group of compartments the openings
should be closed by wire mesh or expanded metal.

3.1.3 *Pipes and cables*
As far as possible pipe lines should be spaced with not less than
50 millimetres between them after allowance for lagging. They should
not be fitted close to a beam flange which might form a secluded shelf.
In arranging pipes and cables care should be taken that the effective
clear headroom as specified in the Regulations is not reduced. Where
pipes pass through non-watertight bulkheads they should be fitted with

collars of either solid steel or wire mesh when not required by these or other Regulations to be provided with other means of closure. Collars should be close fitting and well secured. The protection of casings fitted around cables and the like should be effectively sealed.

3.1.4 *Linings*
Linings should preferably be fitted close to decks and bulkheads, but if not, they should be effectively sealed in such a manner that they do not leave accessible void spaces or present gnawing edges.

3.1.5 *Furniture*
Furniture should be fitted either close against bulkheads and decks or else provided with sufficient space to permit visual inspection. Loose gratings and false bottoms should be avoided.

3.1.6 *Dry provision store rooms*
Too much attention cannot be given to these spaces for it is here that rodents look for food. The boundary bulkheads of dry provision store rooms should be of steel except that bulkheads separating one dry provision storeroom from another may be constructed of wire mesh. The apertures in wire mesh should not exceed 9 millimetres. Doors should be close fitting with suitable stops to prevent rodent entry. All bins should be fitted close against the bulkheads or else far enough away to permit visual inspection. Loose gratings are not to be fitted on the floors (see also paragraph 2.28 above). The shelves should be of open-spaced battens and not of excessive width. If the upper half of the door is intended to be left open for ventilation purposes a closely fitted grating door should be arranged.

3.1.7 *Fresh water and drinking water tanks*
Fresh water and drinking water gravity or service tanks should be so fitted as to provide visual inspection on all sides in addition to the tops and bottoms.

3.1.8 *Galleys*
The same precautions in respect of bulkheads, bins, lockers, etc to those specified for dry provision store rooms in paragraph 3.1.6 apply.

3.1.9 *Washplaces, bathrooms and water closets*
In these spaces only open plumbing should be installed, i.e. pipes should not be boxed-in.

3.1.10 *Ventilation inlets and outlets*
Ventilation inlets and outlets to the open air should be provided with wire mesh the apertures of which do not exceed 9 millimetres.

3.1.11 *Casings*
All casings to telegraph wires, cables, telemotor pipes or any other leads which require protection should be entirely enclosed.

3.2 Liquefied Petroleum Gas domestic installations

Where LPG domestic installations are provided for cooking purposes, heating, lighting, refrigeration, and for the production of hot water or where the Department permits the use of such installations by an exemption from a specific requirement of a regulation the arrangements are to be strictly in accordance with the latest relevant standards. In addition the Surveyor will need to take into account requirements specified in the relevant Fire Protection Regulations.

3.3   Engine room lifts in cargo ships

When considering crew accommodation aspects of lifts between the propulsion machinery spaces and crew accommodation in cargo ships the lifts should in general be constructed to the requirements of the latest relevant standards, and in particular:

.1   it should be impossible in normal operating conditions for doors at more than one level to be open at any one time;

.2   it should not normally be possible to move the lift car under power until the car gate is closed and all the liftwell doors are closed, locked and interlocked;

.3   the doors at each level should be solid steel and self closing;

.4   the lift trunk should be of steel and should be of gastight construction within the confines of the propulsion machinery spaces;

.5   each access opening to the lift within the propulsion machinery spaces should be fitted with either:
   .5.1   a steel gastight self closing door, or
   .5.2   an airlock with two doors, one of which should be of steel, gastight and self-closing;

.6   a notice should be displayed in way of each lift entrance 'Do not use this lift as an emergency escape' and the SWL should be stated.

.7   In addition the Surveyor will need to take into account the requirements of the relevant Fire Protection Regulations.

3.4   Accommodation for repair personnel

Maintenance/repair personnel for regulatory purposes may be classed at owners option as crew or passengers and the requirements as regards accommodation treated accordingly.

3.5   Dry cleaning plants

3.5.1   *General*
Although dry cleaning plants are not required by the Regulation to be provided, where such plants are fitted they should comply with the latest standards, these Instructions and the relevant Merchant Shipping Notices. Only the installation aspects are covered below and it is relevant to note that the requirements outlined are on the assumption that halogenated solvents, which are non-flammable, are to be used in the plant. If patently different machines or solvents are proposed advice should be sought through Marine Directorate DSG1c.

3.5.2 *Hazards*

The principal hazards are associated with the solvents used for dry cleaning. For the ready reference of all concerned with the effective installation of dry cleaning plants with a view to limiting the risk to personnel onboard and to operators of such plants many of the hazards are listed as follows:

.1 The principal hazards associated with dry-cleaning solvent are that it is volatile and the vapour is an anaesthetic. The vapour is capable of inducing drowsiness, followed by unconsciousness and eventually death if the vapour concentration is high enough and the affected person is not quickly removed to fresh air. It is therefore important that effective mechanical ventilation is provided in any compartment containing dry-cleaning plant. The purpose of such ventilation and the following requirements is to ensure that the vapour concentration never exceeds the 'threshold limit value' which is the airborne concentration of vapour under which it is believed that nearly all persons may be repeatedly exposed without adverse affects;

.2 The vapour, if allowed to contact naked flames or red-hot surfaces, decomposes into toxic and corrosive substances which are dangerous to both health and structure. Smoking should therefore be prohibited in compartments where the solvent is present and this is stated in the M Notice.

.3 The solvent, if handled without protective clothing, is a potential cause of de-fatting of the skin, leading to skin cracking with the possibility of infection from other sources;

.4 The vapour is heavier than air, and may therefore build up in the bottom of a compartment in the absence of air currents.

3.5.3 *Position and Access*

3.5.3.1 The plant and associated compartments should be:

.1 positioned wherever practical with an entrance from the open deck;

.2 arranged such that there is no direct communication with crew or passenger accommodation or passageways directly leading thereto;

.3 totally separated from other enclosed spaces by steel gastight divisions;

.4 not used for any other purposes than dry cleaning.

.5 fitted with access doors having sills of 150 millimetre minimum height.

3.5.4 *Ventilation*

.1 A mechanical exhaust fan providing at least 20 changes of air per hour should be fitted to the plant compartment, separate from all other ventilation systems and exhausting to a position in the open air, clear of other accesses, ventilation or window/sidelight openings. The trunk within the compartment is to be equally divided to draw air from:

  .1.1 a high level, and

  .1.2 a level near the deck as close as possible to the plant still; and so positioned that the normal flow of air is directed away from the operator, past the plant and any airing space (see paragraph 3.5.8 below) and thence outboard. If the trunking passes through other compartments then joints within those compartments should be kept to a minimum, care being taken to make them gastight.

.2 The exhaust fan should be

    .2.1 positioned as close to the outboard end of the trunking as practicable, the outboard end being protected from the weather by a fixed baffle;

    .2.2 arranged so that in the event of stoppage of the airflow for any reason, an alarm is given inside and outside the space and the dry cleaning plant becomes inoperable except for the purge fan of the plant, which should be independently controllable. See also paragraph 3.5.9 below;

    .2.3 capable of being started at a position outside the compartment.

.3 If high concentrations of solvent vapour may be discharged from the dry cleaning plant during the purge cycle, the purge fan of the plant should be trunked independently outboard. The same considerations as specified above should be observed for the siting of the outlet and the routeing of the trunk through other compartments.

.4 A balancing vent to atmosphere should be fitted, adequate in size and so sited and diffused that it will not 'short circuit' the main extraction system as described above. The outboard end of the balancing vent should be as remote as possible from the mechanical exhaust from the compartment and the purge outlet. Any mechanical supply ventilation should be separate from all other systems.

3.5.5 *Drainage*
A scupper should be fitted, led directly overboard with no connections to any other drainage system. Scuppers and drain pipes should be of solvent resistant material.

3.5.6 *Water Services*
Any connections with the ship's fresh water system should be suitably protected against contamination by backflow.

3.5.7 *Flooring*
The deck of the compartment should be finished in a material which is impervious to liquids, and resistant to dry cleaning solvents. The decking should be coved up at all sides.

3.5.8 *Clothes airing arrangements*
It is important to provide hanging space with rails where newly cleaned articles should be thoroughly aired before being available for re-use, to remove any solvent fumes. An arrangement of airing space within the plant compartment is acceptable provided such space is adjacent to the exhaust ventilation grilles (both upper and lower), but not so close as to impede the extraction of air from the compartment.

If a separate airing room is provided then ventilation should be as described in paragraph 3.5.4 above, and may utilise the same trunking as the plant room.

3.5.9 *Other Services*
(a) Heating, lighting and heat and sound insulation should be to the standards appropriate to a laundry as specified in the Regulations.

(b) A sensor, which activates an alarm inside and outside the space should the concentration of solvent 'vapour' in the air become unacceptable, is to be fitted in the plant and airing spaces.

3.5.10 *Storage of solvents*

.1 Solvent containers should be kept in a cool place, out of direct sunlight.

.2 No objection will be raised to the storage of three months' supply of solvent in the plant compartment. The solvent should be kept in the manufacturer's containers unless a special bulk storage tank is provided with outside filling arrangements. The manufacturers' containers are to be positively located in strong close-fitting racks to prevent displacement in rough weather, and should be kept sealed until required for use.

.3 If larger quantities of solvent are stored on board ship then a separate compartment should be provided and used for no other purpose. It should be positioned such that access is from an open deck with integrity, drainage, security and solvent containment arrangements as described above.

.4 If the storage capacity either in containers or in purpose-built storage tanks is 20 gallons or more an independent mechanical exhaust ventilation system should be installed, together with a fresh air inlet. Otherwise natural ventilation may be employed comprising a supply to the top of the compartment and an exhaust as low and direct as possible, remote from other vent access openings. The access door to the compartment should in any case have the least possible sill height. A closed vessel should be provided for transferring solvent to the plant compartment.

.5 Each storage position should be provided with a permanent notice identifying the type of solvent suitable for the dry cleaning plant, with a list of the manufacturers and trade names of suitable products. The notice should prohibit the use of other solvents in the plant.

3.5.11 *Emergency equipment*

An approved fire extinguisher of suitable type should be provided for use in the plant compartment, together with means of dealing with minor spillages.

3.6 Temporary Accommodation Units

.1 The standard of accommodation within the unit or module together with the provision of all services should comply with the requirements of the Regulations.

.2 Where .1 is not practical exemptions may be considered giving consideration to type, period, intended area of service etc as relevant.

.3 A suitably protected route shall be provided between the units and the ships permanent crew accommodation facilities.

.4 Other principal relevant regulations are the appropriate Load Line and Fire Regulations.

3.7 Redundant Crew Accommodation

.1 Where it is proposed that the number of crew be reduced on an existing ship, resulting in the closing or change of use of accommodation spaces, it is important to ensure that compliance with the Regulations is maintained. Owners should submit the proposals for consideration before work commences.

.2 Where changes as referred to in .1 above have already taken place a Surveyor should survey/inspect any changes as considered relevant and advise the Master/Owner of any requirements.

3.8 Existing Ships

Existing ships, that is ships which were registered in the United Kingdom before 1 July 1979, should comply with the requirements of Part II of the Regulations. It should be noted that Part II of the Regulations is the same as the Merchant Shipping (Crew Accommodation) Regulations 1953, as amended, except that the exemptions that were specified in each Regulation have been deleted. Exemptions already granted will remain under normal circumstances in force.

3.9 Reports on Completion of Survey

3.9.1 *General*
Following the completion of the survey of any ship with reference to the requirements of the Regulations the Surveyor should record on the particular ships CM 23/01 file his 'Completion Report'. This Report when referred to in conjunction with other minutes, correspondence and plans on the file should confirm that the duties of the Department have been properly discharged in respect of the Regulations.

3.9.2 *Format of Report*
The format should be such that as appropriate the following is recorded or referred to, to facilitate ready reference:—

.1 All relevant particulars of the ship

.2 If exemptions from the Regulations have been applied for and agreed, confirmation that the conditions of the exemptions (as indicated on the agreed SUR 184) are or will be complied with.

.3 Principal matters 'dealt with' during the survey.

.4 Completion tests undertaken and results' obtained, including any noise measurements.

.5 Any 'unusual points' of the case considered worthy of particular note.

.6 Confirmation that the ship as completed complies with the Regulations, subject to any exemptions agreed as para (.2) above, and that the arrangements; materials and equipment comply with and are fitted in accordance with all relevant requirements and to the Surveyors satisfaction.

3.9.3 *Processing the CM 23/01 file*

.1 Where exemptions from the Regulations have been formally applied for and agreed, see paragraph 1.7, the file including the surveyors completion report in accordance with the above should be forwarded to Marine Directorate DSG1c to facilitate the issue of a SUR185 confirming to the shipowner the exemptions agreed and the conditions of such agreement.

.2 Where .1 above is not applicable the file may be forwarded through the Chief Surveyor of the District directly to registry for putting away unless it is considered necessary to refer Marine Directorate DSG1c to particular aspects of the case.

ANNEX 1

Fresh Water Produced on Board Ship

General Requirements and Listing of Approved Equipment and Water Treatments

This Annex outlines the procedures and conditions associated with the approval and use of equipment for the production of fresh water on board UK registered ships in accordance with the Regulations.

In addition to the Regulations and these Instructions the Merchant Shipping (Provisions and Water) Regulations 1988 are also relevant.

Contents   Page

List

1. Low Pressure Evaporators

1.1 The Department is prepared to approve particular evaporating and distilling plant for the production of fresh domestic water on board UK registered ships given satisfactory information relevant to (a) and (b) below, see also guidance notes para 2 onward.

.1 the adequacy or otherwise of the design to withstand the pressures to which it might be subject in service, and the provision of over-pressure safeguards and;

.2 the ability, in the context of the Merchant Shipping (Crew Accommodation) Regulations 1978 to produce fresh water acceptable for domestic purposes.

1.2 Prototype designs of plant for which approval is required should be submitted to Marine Directorate for consideration of both (a) and (b) of paragraph 1.

.2.1 The actual designation of the plants for which acceptance is required should be made known.

.2.2 Diagrammatic arrangement plans for each plant should be forwarded together with detailed engineering drawings of the high pressure pump, relief valves, pressure valves (including membrane modules), tanks and flow control design so that the Department can adequately assess the strength and suitability of these items. Details of materials, bores or outside diameters, wall thicknesses and flanges of rigid pipes and particulars of all flexible pipes should also be submitted for consideration.

The Department will require to witness pressure and functional tests on the above mentioned items.

.2.3 In respect of electrical matters, the following information is required:—
   a. A schematic circuit diagram.
   b. Full details of make and rating of all fuses, contactors, switches, overload relays and other control components.
   c. Full details of each pump meter with a copy of the manufactuer's type test certificates.
   d. Confirmation that all components are constructed to the relevant British Standard (or equivalent).
   e. Details of cables/wiring used (size and type of insulation).

All electric equipment should comply with the Regulation for the Electrical and Electronic Equipment of Ships, 1972 Edition, issued by the Institution of Electrical Engineers.

.2.4 Installation, operational and maintenance manuals for each plant should be forwarded.

.2.5 Where chemicals are to be used for either the pre-treatment of the feed water or in cleaning cycles of the membranes etc full details of these should be given including the strength, dosage rate and basic chemical compositions.

.2.6 The production of drinking water by the plant should be witnessed by the Department's Surveyor or appointed Surveyor at the manufacturers works and samples forwarded to an independent analyst for complete chemical and bacteriological examination. The pH value should also be determined. In regard to these tests the plant should be operated using good clean sea water to ensure that the plant will remove salt and then operated using polluted type deck water to demonstrate its capabilities.

1.3   As to installation in ships, 1(a) is normally a matter for the Classification Society concerned to deal with, as it deals with other pressure containers on board, but if the vessel is not classed, the arrangements of the evaporating and distilling plant should be submitted to the Department in respect of 1(a). So far as 1(b) is concerned, in all ships, no submission is necessary (i) if the plant has already been approved (list D or (ii) if the heating medium of the plant is steam above atmospheric pressure.

1.4   The water from which the distillate is produced is to be taken from a pump used exclusively for sea water service. Such a connection may be made from the discharge side of the pump if the bore of the discharge pipe is 75 millimetres or over. No connection is to be taken from the discharge side of any heat exchanger, or similar vessel, which may provide a source of contamination.

1.5   Typical Conditions of Approval (Evaporators)

.5.1   A copy of the manufacturer's installation, operation and servicing manual is to be supplied with each generator.

.5.2   Water intended for domestic purposes is to be effectively treated after manufacture by an automatic chlorination plant or alternatively disinfected by a unit and/or method approved by the Department.

.5.3   The plants are not to be used in water in which weed or other organisms are present and in water affected by estuarial discharge and in any case a 20 mile limit from any coast must be observed. A notice to this effect is to be fixed to each plant and this information is to be stated in the manual referred to in 1 above.

.5.4   The water from which the distillate is to be produced is to be taken from a pump used exclusively for sea water service. Such a connection may be made from the discharge side of the pump if the bore of the discharge pipe is 75 mm or over. Where the product water is intended for drinking purposes no connection is to be taken from the discharge side of any heat exchanger or similar vessel, which may provide a source of contamination.

.5.5   Every generator for installation in a passenger ship should be manufactured under the Department's survey. Generators for installation in cargo ships should be manufactured either under the Department's survey or under the survey of a Classification Society recognised by the Department.

.5.6   On installation satisfactory operation tests should be witnessed by a Department's surveyor.

.5.7   Spare parts not less than the manufacturer's minimum recommended spares list are to be carried for each plant.

.5.8   The arrangement at ship i.e. piping and valves should comply with the Load Line Rules.

.5.9   This acceptance is based on the information supplied by the manufacturer and on the understanding that this Department reserves the right to require check tests of the plants to be made at any time.

.5.10 No modification to the plants will be permitted without the prior consent of the Department of Transport.

2. Reverse Osmosis Desalination Plants

2.1 The Department is prepared to approve particular RO desalination plant for the production of fresh domestic water on board UK registered ships given satisfactory information is submitted to Marine Directorate as follows.

2.2 The actual designation of the plants for which acceptance is required should be made known.

2.3 Diagrammatic arrangement plants for each plant should be forwarded together with detailed engineering drawings of the high pressure pump, relief valves, filters, pressure vessels (including membrane modules) tanks and flow control design so that the Department can adequately assess the strength and suitability of these items. Details of materials, bores or outside diameters, wall thicknesses and flanges of rigid pipes and particulars of all flexible pipes should also be submitted for consideration.

A hydraulic test to destruction or to $6 \times$ working pressure on a prototype membrane fibre glass filter chamber should be witnessed by a Department Surveyor, or by an independent surveyor.

The Department will require to witness functional tests on the plant including hydraulic tests on the system. All line filters on the high and low pressure sides are to be tested to $2 \times$ working Presure and Piping should be subjected to the following:—

LP side $1.5 \times$ WP
HP side $1.3 \times$ Max WP

2.4 In respect of electrical matters, the following information is required:—
   a. A schematic circuit diagram.
   b. Full details of make and rating of all fuses, contactors, switches, overload relays and other control components.
   c. Full details of each pump meter with a copy of the manufacturer's type test certificates.
   d. Confirmation that all components are constructed to the relevant British Standard (or equivalent).
   e. Details of cables/wiring used (size and type of insulation).

All electric equipment should comply with the Regulation for the Electrical and Electronic Equipment of Ships, 1972 Edition, issued by the Institution of Electrical Engineers.

2.5 Installation, operational and maintenance manuals for each plant should be forwarded.

2.6 The actual value in mg/L to which it is proposed to set the salinometer should be stated [this should be not greater than 500 mg/L for chloride.]

2.7   The chemical composition of the membranes should be accurately stated. The actual type of membranes being used should be made known.

2.8   Where chemicals are to be used for either the pre-treatment of the feed water or in cleaning cycles of the membranes etc full details of these should be given including the strength, dosage rate and basic chemical compositions.

2.9   The production of drinking water by the plant should be witnessed by the Department's Surveyor or appointed Surveyor at the manufacturers works and samples forwarded to an independent analyst for complete chemical and bacteriological examination. The pH value should also be determined. In regard to these tests the plant should be operated using good clean sea water to ensure that the plant will remove salt and then operated using polluted type deck water to demonstrate its capabilities for consideration and record. See details of test procedures at C.

2.10   The manuals referred to in (5) above should contain at the beginning the following statement:

'The plant is not to be used in waters in which weed or other organisms are present and in waters affected by esturial discharge and in any case a 20 mile limit from any coast must be observed'.

2.11   Typical Conditions of Approval (RO Plant)

In accepting of RO plants it will be necessary for the Department to lay down conditions which are outlined below. The manufacturer should indicate that he agrees to abide by these before formal acceptance is given.

11.1   The manufacturer or agents appointed by them are to give the shipbuilder, for ships intended for United Kingdom registry, all the technical data available to ensure that plants will be correctly installed and effectively operated.

11.2   A set of manufacturers instructions covering fully the installation, operation and maintenance of the plant is to be supplied with each plant.

11.3   No bypass is to be fitted by the shipbuilder around the plant or any connection provided which could enable a temporary bypass to be arranged.

11.4   The feed pump should be solely used for supplying the plant and should not be used for any other purpose.

11.5   The salinometer should be set at the manufacturers works so that product water does not contain more than 500 mg/L of chloride. The arrangement for control should be such that the ships staff cannot alter or vary the setting.

11.6   After installation of the plant it should run for 30 minutes the water being produced during this time being dumped so as to ensure that the plant is clean and free from impurities. The precaution should also be observed when any part of the plant, including piping is dismantled for maintenance etc.

11.7   The plant is not to be used in waters in which weed or other organisms are present and in waters affected by esturial discharge and in any case a 20 miles limit from any coast must be observed. A notice is to be fixed to each plant conveying this information.

11.8 When membranes are replaced only ....
.... manufactured by .... are to be fitted.

11.9 Water intended for domestic purposes is to be effectively treated after manufacture by an automatic chlorination plant or alternatively disinfected by a unit and/or method approved by the Department.

11.10 Spare parts not less than the manufacturers minimum recommended spares list are to be carried for each plant fitted and the owners notified that they are to obtain at least the standard kit on each occasion that renewal of the membranes is necessary. Spare membranes should be carried on any ship fitted with reverse osmosis plants on the basis of one spare membrane for every 10 membranes or part thereof contained in a plant. This scale of spares is to be applied for each spearate plant.

11.11 The installation of each plant should be surveyed by the Department's surveyors.

11.12 The arrangement at ship i.e. piping and valves should comply with the Merchant Shipping (Load Line) Rules 1968.

11.13 Every generator for installation in a passenger ship should be manufactured under the Department's survey. Generators for installation in cargo ships should be manufactured either under the Department's survey or under the survey of a Classification Society recognised by the Department.

11.14 This acceptance is based on the information supplied by the manufacturer and on the understanding that this Department reserves the right to require check tests of the plant to be made at any time.

11.15 No modification to the plant will be permitted without the prior consent of the Department of Transport.

11.16 Where it is known that plants are intended for United Kingdom registered ships the manufacturer is to convey the above conditions to the shipbuilder.

3. Chemical and bacteriological tests on samples of water

Note: These are to be carried out by or on behalf of the manufacturers or installers of the fresh water making plant

3.1 Procedure

A record giving the following information is to be signed by the person in charge of the test for the plant makers and countersigned by the ship's master and Chief Engineer and forwarded with the samples for testing:
    (a)   Name of ship and owners etc;
    (b)   Identification of plant;
    (c)   Capacity of plant (name plate with these particulars should be fitted);

(d) Confirmation that the samples of water have been drawn off before any chlorination or filtration (except gauze or mechanical strainer) is made;

(e) Log of times of starting up plant, tests and completion, etc;

(f) Two samples of the distillate for chemical examination and two for bacteriological examination should be taken at any time when the ship is more than 20 miles from land but must not be taken less than an hour apart, one sample for chemical test and one for bacteriological test may be taken at the same time;

(g) Position of ship at the time of each test;

(h) The samples should be sent to the Government Chemist for analysis (or to Public Health or other equivalent Authority if the vessel is abroad). If the samples for bacteriological examination cannot be despatched so as to arrive with the Government Chemist within 48 hours they should be submitted to a local independent analyst whose report should be sent to the Marine Directorate for consideration.

Check on the capacity of the plant by the actual quantity of fresh water produced and how measured, over a set period.

Name of ship, date and time taken are to be stated on the bottle label for each sample.

3.2 DESIRABLE DETERMINANDS

CHEMICAL EXAMINATION

E — Essential
O — Optional
* — Only if chlorine is added

Ammonium nitrogen as NH_4 (mg/l)	E
Kjeldahl nitrogen as N (mg/l)	E
Nitrate nitrogen as NO_3 (mg/l)	E
Nitrite nitrogen as NO_2 (mg/l)	E
Total alkalinity as HCO_3 (mg/l)	O
Total hardness as Ca (mg/l)	E
Total organic carbon (mg/l)	O
Sulphate as SO_4 (mg/l)	O
Chloride (mg/l)	E
Free residual chlorine (mg/l)	E*
Total residual chlorine (mg/l)	E*
Fluoride (mg/l)	O
Phosphorus as P_2O_5 (mg/l)	O
Aluminium (mg/l)	O
Calcium (mg/l)	O
Magnesium (mg/l)	O
Potassium (mg/l)	O
Sodium (mg/l)	E
Cadmium (mg/l)	E
Chromium (mg/l)	O
Cobalt (mg/l)	O
Copper (mg/l)	E
Iron (mg/l)	E
Lead (mg/l)	E

Manganese (mg/l)	O
Mercury (mg/l)	O
Nickel (mg/l)	E
Zinc (mg/l)	E

PHYSICAL EXAMINATION

pH	E
Conductivity (siemens/cm at 20°C)	O
Clarity	O
Colour	O
Odour	O
Sediment	O

BACTERIOLOGICAL EXAMINATION

No colonies/ml on nutrient agar:

| | (a) | 37°C/1 day | E |
| | (b) | 22°C/3 days | E |

MPN/100 ml:

	(a)	Coliaerogenes	E
	(b)	Escherichia coli	E
	(c)	Faecal streptococci	O

MPN/20 ml: S-R Clostridia   O

4. Electrolitic Silver Release Fresh Water Disinfection Systems

The Department accepts electro-silver ionisation systems for the automatic disinfecting of fresh water *produced on board* United Kingdom registered ships.

A summary of the conditions of acceptance which are applicable to the fitting of such disinfection systems is given below.

.1 Any proposal for fitting a system on a passenger class UK registered ship is to be submitted to the Marine Directorate for individual consideration.

.2 The manufacturers or agents appointed by them, are required to supervise the installation of any units, supplied for ships intended for United Kingdom registry, to ensure that they are fitted in accordance with their detailed instructions.

.3 A set of manufacturer's instructions covering fully the installation, operation and maintenance of the disinfection systems should be filed with the Department for record and supplied with each unit for the reference of the operators.

.4 The disinfection unit is to be fitted in the fresh water system between the production unit and the storage tanks, as near to the former as is practicable and in a readily accessible position.

.5 Each system is to be designed for the maximum flow rate of the fresh water production unit.

.6 'Fail safe' operation of the disinfection units is to be achieved by fitting an automatic, normally closed solenoid operated valve in the system. The valve is to be under the independent control of the electrode monitor such that the valve will close and prevent the passage of water into the storage-distribution system should the unit malfunction in any way.

.7 An audible visible automatic alarm should be installed connected to the 'Fail Safe' control system and should give a warning of failure of power supply or any malfunction of the disinfection unit causing closure of the solenoid operated valve. The electricity supply required to operate the alarm should be independent of the supply to the disinfection unit.

.8 No facility for by-passing the disinfection unit is to be fitted or provided.

.9 The design setting of each unit is to be checked by the manufacturers before despatch and is to be such as to ensure that a minimum of 0.1 ppm silver concentration will be added to the water produced under maximum flow conditoins.

.10 The fresh water storage and distribution system should be designed such that the silver contact time with the water is a minimum of 4 hours before use.

.11 Any water 'conditioning' units should be installed after the disinfecting unit and before storage.

.12 Spare parts not less than the manufacturer's minimum spares list (see manufacturer's instructions) are to be carried for each unit fitted.

.13 Acceptance is based on the information supplied by the manufacturer and is subject to the system operating satisfactorily in service. The Department reserves the right to require check tests to be made at any time.

5. Miscellaneous

Filters, water softeners and the like, are normally not subject to approval/acceptance procedures, however, whenever it is intended that the domestic water should be 'treated' using equipment incorporating materials and/or chemicals likely to affect the acceptability and/or quality of the water then suitable samples of 'treated' water should be submitted through the Marine Directorate for consideration and clearance by the Government Chemist.

LIST A

Approved Fresh Water Low Pressure Generators

Name and Address of Manufacturer	Name of Product	File No	MDM No	Date of Expiry
Alfa Laval Co Ltd	JW Type	MS47/2/015		1.1.1996
Great West Road	JWP Type			1.1.1996
Brentford	JWFP Type			1.1.1996
Middlesex	F Type	MS47/2/068		1.1.1996
	Compact S Type			1.1.1996
	JWSP-36-C125	MC25/9/0477	212/87	21.1.1997
	JSWP-36-125	MS47/2/068	157/76	1.1.1996
	JSWP-36-150	MS47/2/068	157/76	
	JSWP-36-200	MS47/2/068	157/76	
	JSWP-26-050/C100	MC25/9/0514	311/87	9.10.1997
Buckau-Walther AG	SE V sw 25/32	MS47/2/060	—	1.1.1996
Postfach 210120				
2800 Bremen 21				
West Germany				
Buckley & Taylor Ltd	Aquagenerator	MS47/2/016		1.1.1996
Castle Iron Works				
Oldham				
Lancs				
OL4 1HJ				
Caird + Rayner-	Movac No 4 Sile	MC25/9/073		1.1.1996
Bravac Ltd	Vertical			
Otterspool Way	Vavac Mk VII	MS47/11/0239		1.1.1996
Watford By Pass	Vaflash	MC25/9/0144		1.1.1996
Watford	Movac Mk II	MC25/9/073	211/87	2.2.1997
WD2 8HL	CS3	Pt 2		
	CS2, CS4, CS5			
	Design Approval			
Chadburns Ltd				
Fabryka Urzodzen	WY 32	MC25/9/0429	—	
Okretowych	WY 63A			
Rumia	WY 63AP			
UL Sobieskiego Nr 42	WY 125A			1.1.1996
Wojewodztwo	WY 250A			
Gdanskie	WY 400A			
Poland				
George Clark & Sons	JW 60	MC25/9/086	144/79	1.1.1996
Ltd	JW 150	MS2/47/2/079		1.1.1996
Hawthorn Avenue	JW 250	MS2/47/2/079		1.1.1996
Hull	JW 30	MS2/47/2/079		1.1.1996
Humberside				
Nirex Engineers Ltd	JSWP-36-125			1.1.1996
(Alfa-Laval Group)	JWSP-36-150			1.1.1996
20-Metalbuen	JWSP-36-200			1.1.1996
DK-2750 Ballerup	JWSP-36C-100/125			1.1.1996
Denmark	JWSP-36-150DE			1.1.1996
	JWSP-36-200DE			1.1.1996
Krupp Industrielechnik	SEV 25/32			
GmbH				
Postfach 21 01 20				1.1.1996
2800 Bremen 21				
W Germany				
Jedinstvo	AFGU Type EO.5-1	MC25/9/0403		1.1.1996
PO Box 371	Type EO.5-2 under			
Samborska 145	S21 licence			
41001 Zagreb-Susegrad	S31-81 from			
Yogoslavia	S32-82 Atlas			
	E21 Denmark			
	E31-61			

Name and Address of Manufacturer	Name of Product	File No	MDM No	Date of Expiry
Sasakura Engineer Co Ltd 7–5 Mitejima 6 Chome Nishlyodogana-Ku Osaka 555 Japan	Afgu 2(N) Afgu 3(N) Afgu 4(N) Afgu 5(N) Afgu 6(N) Afgu 7(N) Afgu 8(N) Afgu 5(A) Afgu S31 Afgu S41 Afgu S51 Afgu S61 Afgu S71 Afgu S81 Afgu S32 Afgu S42 Afgu S52 Afgu S62 Afgu S72 Afgu S82 Afgu E–0.5 Afgu E–1 Afgu E–2 Afgu E–3 Afgu E–4 Afgu E–0.5–1 Afgu E–0.5–2 Afgu 521 ⎫ made under Afgu E31–62 ⎬ licence from Afgu E21 ⎭ Atlas 　　　　　　Denmark	MC25/9/0370 Pt 1	205/85	1.1.1996
	KE3–KE60	MC25/9/0370	206/88	15.1.98
Fabryka Urzadzen 　Okretowych 84–230 Rumia	WY32 WY400			1.1.1996 1.1.1996
Thune Eureka PO Box 28 N–3401 Lier Norway	FWG–30			1.1.1996
Atlas-Denmark A/S	AFGU Type 0.5–1 E 0.5–2 S 21 S 32–82 E 21 E 31–61			1.1.1996 1.1.1996 1.1.1996 1.1.1996 1.1.1996 1.1.1996
	AFGU Range of single and double effect	MC25/9/0403	374/87	20.11.97

LIST B

Approved Reverse Osmosis Plants

Name and Address of Manufacturer	Name of Product	MDM No	Official Ref	Approval expiry date
Ames Crosta Babcock Ltd Gregge Street Heywood Lancashire OL10 2DX	Series 2½ Series 5 Series 20 Series 75	241/87	MC25/9/0447	
Aqua-Chem Inc PO Box 421 Milwaukee Winsconsin 53201 USA	Acro Pac	246/84	MC25/9/0427	
George Clark & Sons (Hull) Ltd Hawthorn Avenue	20 Tons/Day 75 Tons/Day	203/84	MC25/9/0452	
	50 Tons/Day	203/84	MC25/9/0469	
	10 Tons/Day	202/84	MC25/9/0475	
	Series 200–100/200 Series 600–300/600 Series 3000–1000/4000		MC25/9/0413	
Caird & Rayner-Bravac Ltd Otterspool Way Watford By Pass Watford WD2 8HL	8 Tons/Day 30 Tons/Day		MC25/9/0511 MC25/9/0530	
Reverse Osmosis Systems Ltd Westgate Hill Tonge West Yorkshire BD4 0SJ	ROS 220 Series ROS 300–500 M3/Day	338/87 361/87	MC25/9/0532 MC25/9/0514 MC25/9/0554	 3.11.1997
Rochem R-O Desalination Ltd Knightsbridge House 229 Acton Lane London W4 5DD	RoRo 5s RoRo 10s RoRo 15s RoRo 20s RoRo 25s RoRo 30s RoRo 40s RoRo 50s RoRo 60s RoRo 70s RoRo 80s Ro 5s to Ro 80s	 373/87	MC25/9/0483 MC25/9/0483	 11.11.97

LIST C

Approved Corrosion Inhibitors

Manufacturer's Name and Address	Name of Product	Max Permitted Dosage From Toxic Considerations	File No
Atlas Products & Services Ltd Fraser Road Erith Kent DA8 1PN	Atlas Collex CI Corrosion Inhibitor	2 gallons to every 100 gallons of cooling water	MC25/9/0105
	Atlas Collex CIA Corrosion Inhibitor	2% of total volume of water	MC25/9/024
Bacillofabrik Dr Bode & Co Bode Laboratories (UK) 327A Lillie Road Fulham Cross Fulham London SW6 7NR	Ebotec-Aqua	0.05%–2% dosage rate	MC25/9/044
Bull & Roberts Inc 785 Central Avenue Murray Hill NJ 07974 USA	Corrosion Inhibitor CS	As prescribed in Bulletin CS-367	MC25/9/0214
Burmah-Castrol Marin Burmah House Pipers Way Swindon Wiltshire	Castrol Solvex WT2	2% by volume	MC25/9/0204
	Castrol Solvex WT4	0.3% by weight	
Drew Ameroid (UK) Ltd Marlowe House Station Road Sidcup Kent DA15 7EP	Dewt-NC	7lbs per ton of circulating water	MC25/9/0140 MC25/9/0184
	Drewgard 100	5000 ppm	
	Maxigard	Maximum—2% of cooling water	MC25/9/0184
	Liquidewt	Nitrate or nitrite concentration not to exceed 50 or 0.1 mgl 1 respectively	MC25/9/0184
Foss Laboratories 28 Halkett Place Jersey CI	Foss 2217	1 gallon to 80 tons of freshwater	MC25/9/088
Atlas Products & Services Gamlen Chemical Co (UK) Ltd Wallingford Road Uxbridge Middlesex	Atlas Collex CI	2 gallons to every	MC25/9/0105
	Gamcor 1770	1,000 ppm	MC25/9/086
	Gamcor NB	1,200 ppm	MC25/9/086
	Gamlen 57M	1%	MC25/9/086
	Gamcor 1308	1,000 to 2,000 ppm dosage	MC25/9/086
Mobil Oil Co Ltd Coryton Stanford le Hope Essex	Solvac 1535	0.5% to 0.7% by volume	MC25/9/0120
Nalfloc Ltd PO Box No 11 Northwich Cheshire	Nalfleet 9-121	2,500 ppm	MC25/9/0106
	Nalfleet 9-111	14½–22 pints per ton	MC25/9/0165
	Nalfleet 9-131C	14½–22 pints per ton	MC25/9/0165
	Nalfleet 9-108		MC25/9/0165
	Nalcool 2000	11 per 321 coolant	MC25/9/0165

Manufacturer's Name and Address	Name of Product	Max Permitted Dosage From Toxic Considerations	File No
Perolin Co Ltd Brimscombe Mill Brimscombe Stroud Gloucester	Formet 336	2,500 ppm	MC25/9/0162
	Inhibitin	1% by volume	MC25/9/0162
	Antifoul 326	As per Technical Bulletin No MF–326	MC25/9/0162
Rochem UK Ltd Unit 2 Maskell Industrial Estate Stephenson Street London E16	Evaporator Treatment 2343		
	Rochem Rocor NB	Not to exceed 2,000 ppm as Nitrite (NO_2)	MC25/9/0257
Shell UK Oil Shell-Mex House Strand London WC2R 0DX	Shell Dromus Oil B	1%	MC25/9/011
	Shell Dromus Oil E	0.75%	MC25/9/011
	Shell Dromus Oil D	0.5%	MC25/9/011
Sterling Industrial Chapeltown Sheffield S30 4YP	Parmetol K40	0.05–0.15%	MC25/9/0459
Atlas Products & Services Timmons and Charles Inc 991 East Linden Ave PO Box 507 Linden New Jersey 07036 USA	Atlas Collex CI T&C Diesel Water Treatment (Non-Chromate)	2 gallons to every 7lbs per 100 galls of cooling water	MC25/9/0105 MC25/9/0296
Tokyo Crystal Hanbai Co Ltd 8–6 Koraku 2-Chome Bunkyo-Ku Tokyo Japan	Nikkuri 25 S	25 g per ton of water supply	
Vecom-Houseman Marine 5 Lexham Court Maidenhead Berkshire SL6 1QN	Cooltreat 101	2.5 kg/m^3	MC25/9/0293
	Cooltreat 102	5 litres/m^3	MC25/9/0293
	Oxytreat 10	up to 160mg/litres	MC25/9/0293
	Alkatreat 2	up to 1000mg/litre	MC25/9/0293
	DM 4–1 Concentrate	1 litre/m^3	MC25/9/0142
	C-Treat 6	8mg/1	MC25/9/0399

LIST D

Approved Scale Inhibitors

Manufacturer's Name and Address	Name of Product	Max Permitted Dosage From Toxic Considerations	File No
Atlas Products & Service Ltd Fraser Road Erith Kent DA18 1PN	Atlas HTT Evaporator Treater Liquid	25 mg to 1 litre of feed water	MC25/9/0204
	Atlas Collex CIS Inhibitor	2% of total vol of water	MC25/9/0204
Buckman Laboratories Zondelgamkaai 157 B-9000 Ghent Belgium	SASE (BUSPERSE 49)	5–150 ppm	MC25/9/0200
Burmah Castrol Marine Burmah House Pipers Way Swindon Wiltshire	Castrol Solvex WT9	Not to exceed 25 mg/1 water	MC25/9/0204
	Castrol Solvex WT8	4–5 ppm in seawater feed	
Drew Chemical (UK) Ltd Marlowe House Station Road Sidcup Kent	Ameroyal	1oz per ton distillate	MC25/9/0140
Gamlen Chemical Co (UK) Ltd	Gamavap	10 mg/litre	MC25/9/0359
Wallingford Road Uxbridge Middlesex	Gamcool CWT	101 per 10001	MC25/9/0359
Nalfloc Ltd PO Box No 11	Nalfleet	10mg/litre	MC25/9/0181
Mond House Winnington Northwich Cheshire	Nalfleet 9–920 Maxivap (with antifoam)		MC25/9/0181
Perolin Co Ltd Brimscombe Mill Brimscombe	Formet 343	30cc per ton of distillate daily	MC25/9/0181
Stroud Gloucester	Format 344	100 mg/1	MC25/9/0181
Rochen UK Ltd Unit 2 Maskell Industrial Estate Stephenson Street London E16	Rochen Vaptreat Liquid	10 mg/1	MC25/9/0257
Atlas Products & Services	Atlas Collex CI	2 gallons to every	MC25/9/0105
Vecom-Houseman Marine 5 Lexham Court	Vaptreat H	25 mg/litre	MC25/9/0159
High Street Maidenhead Berkshire SL6 1QN	Alkatreat 2	up to 1000mg/litre	MC25/9/0293

LIST E

Approved Disinfecting Systems for Domestic Fresh Water

Manufacturer's Name and Address	Disinfection Agent	Dosage Requirements	Method of Dosing	Restrictions	File No
Various	Chlorine	Such that residual free chlorine content of 0.2 ppm is achieved	Manually or by suitable automatic unit(s) as required	None	MC25/15/039
Katadyn Products Inc Wallisellen Switzerland	Silver	0.1 ppm at on board production point	Automatically using Electro-Katadyn Units 4, 24 or 72	Only for use with shipboard produced fresh water see also para 1.5	MC25/9/070

Deck Covering (including underside of deck)
General Requirements and Listing of Accepted Coverings

This Annex outlines the procedures and conditions associated with the approval and use of deck coverings on UK registered ships in accordance with the Regulations and these Instructions.

In addition to the Regulations and these Instructions the following regulations and related Instructions are relevant:

(i)   The Merchant Shipping (Crew Accommodation) (Fishing Vessels) Regulations 1975. Schedule 1;

(ii) The Fishing Vessels (Safety Provisions) Rules 1975. Rules 1(5), 56(11), 57(10) and 58(9);

(iii) The Merchant Shipping (Fire Protection) Regulations 1984. Regs 1(2), 54(2)(d), 100(2)(d), 121(2) and 138(2)

Contents

4. Coverings on the underside of weather decks which are crowns of crew accommodation

    4.1   General

5. Decks exposed to appreciable heat or cold

    5.1   General

6. Floors of hospitals and similar spaces

    6.1   General

7. Floors of bathrooms, washplaces, water closets and similar spaces

    7.1   General

Appendix A Acceptance of Deck Coverings—Requirements relating to ignitability, toxicity and explosive hazards

Appendix B Approved floorings and Underlays in Crew Accommodation

Appendix C Approved coverings for the Underside of Weather Decks Forming the Crowns of Crew Accommodation

Appendix D Approved coverings for the Topside of Weather Decks Forming the Crowns of Crew Accommodation

Appendix E Approved coatings for use under coverings of the Magnesium Oxychloride Type or under coverings on the crowns of oil tanks.

1.   Approval

1.1   Definition

Deck covering as referred to herein may be

    .1.1   A composition underlay or final surface finish material is to be laid on a suitable underlay on the topside of decks, in way of crew accommodation spaces, in compliance with the Regulations and Schedule 1, or

    .1.2   A covering fitted on the upper or underside of overhead decks exposed to the weather and in way of crew accommodation spaces in compliance with the Regulations and Schedule 2.

1.2   General

    .2.1   The Department is prepared to approve particular deck coverings as defined in 1. above, subject to conditions indicated on any approval document issued and which will include 'subject to the deck covering providing satisfactory in service'.

    .2.2   Formal approval will not be given for coverings solely for use in sanitary accommodation, galleys and laundaries in compliance with the Regulations. In such cases acceptance on a specific ship will be given by a Surveyor at the ship, taking into account their suitability.

.2.3 Acceptance of a covering is subject to the condition that in composition, weight and other properties, it does not differ from the sample tested.

.2.4 The Department reserves the right to withdraw acceptance if the material proves unsatisfactory in service, or if the conditions attached to the acceptance are not observed.

.2.5 If a manufacturer ceases to manufacture an accepted covering he should notify the Department immediately.

1.3 Procedures

Submissions requesting approval, should be prepared by the Manufacturer and forwarded to DSG1C Branch of the Department for consideration. They should include:

.3.1 Full details of the intended use of the material and the methods of laying to be adopted.

.3.2 a specification of the constituents of the material, the proportions being given by weight.

.3.3 Two samples (or more), representing the methods of laying proposed, at least 150 mm × 150 mm attached to 3 mm thick steel plating.

Note (i) In the case of a finished deck covering this should be superimposed on a suitable underlay where an underlay is appropriate.

(ii) In the case of a multi-layer deck covering including floating decks, the sample should fully represent the deck covering as is intended to be laid.

.3.4 Independent laboratory reports of tests confirming the characteristics of the material as required by the relevant Regulations, Schedules and these Instructions, see also paragraph 2.

.3.5 A deposit on fees.

(i) Note fees are charged on the basis of surveyor hours subject to a minimum of 3 hours for the 'straight forward' case.

2. Material Characteristics

2.1 General

Unless otherwise agreed all tests are to be undertaken by a recognised independent laboratory at the Manufacturers expense.

2.2 Good foothold and easily kept clean.

To date these features have been assessed from consideration of the samples provided and in service reports where necessary. However if relevant test data is available this should be submitted for record and consideration.

2.3 Thermal conductivity

2.3.1 General

.1.1 Materials for use on decks which are exposed to the weather and also the crowns of crew and passenger accommodation are to be tested for thermal conductivity.

.1.2 For the purpose of comparison the thermal conductivity of wood may be taken as 0.124 kilocalorie per square metre per hour for one metre thickness and one degree centigrade difference in temperature between the faces (k cal/m h deg C).

.1.3 Coverings fitted within accommodation spaces need not in general be tested for thermal conductivity, but the materials should be such as will provide a warm and comfortable surface. This will be assessed from samples submitted.

2.3.2 Method of testing

.2.1 Test samples which should be 300 mm × 300 mm × 38 mm to 50 mm thick are to be placed one on each side of a hot plate, the whole being clamped between two cold plates maintained at a constant temperature.

.2.2 The temperatures of the hot and cold surfaces are to be measured by means of thermocouples. Heat input to the hot plate is to be obtained by observation of the watts dissipated in its heating coil.

.2.3 The results are to be expressed in kilocalories transmitted per square metre per hour for one metre thickness and one degree Centigrade difference in temperature (k cal/m h deg C).

2.4 Fire Standards

2.4.1 Non-Ignitability

See also the 'Fire Protection Instructions', however for ready reference see Appendix A which is reproduced here for ready reference.

2.4.2 Non-combustibility

See also the 'Fire Protection Instructions', noting that formal approval with regard to the classifying of a material as non-combustible is dealt with by DSG2C in Sunley House.

2.5 Water absorption

2.5.1 General

.1.1 Coverings of the foamed concrete type or those containing magnesium oxychloride are not considered suitable for use on decks exposed to the weather.

.1.2 For certain coverings it will be necessary to incorporate expansion joints at each edge of the covering where it abuts deck houses or coamings, and this joint is to be covered with a suitable coved fillet.

.1.3 If the covering is in more than one layer a waterproof membrane, or other material suitable for the purpose, or other effective arrangement may be adopted so as to ensure that if the upper layer or layers as the case may be cracks the remainder of the covering will not become saturated in the course of service.

2.5.2 Method of Testing
.2.1 Test samples are to be 150 mm × 50 mm × 50 mm unless, owing to the nature of the material, this is unsuitable. The surface of the samples should not be painted or coated.

.2.2 For the purpose of this test two samples of the material are to be weighed, immersed in water for 48 hours and then weighed again. They are then to be dried to a constant weight. The report of test should show the moisture content before and after immersion expressed as a percentage of the dry weight.

.2.3 If the covering is in more than one layer, unless constructed in an agreed manner as para 2.5.1(c) above, each layer should be tested separately.

2.5.3 Acceptable Standard
.3.1 In the case of a covering to be used within crew accommodation, if the material is otherwise satisfactory but owing to its nature it is not practicable to keep the moisture content to the required figure the results will be considered on their merits.

2.6 Health and Safety

The materials used for deck coverings should not be likely to have any injurious effect on personnel during laying or on crew and passengers in service.

2.7 Resistance to wear

The materials are required to be sufficiently hard and tough to stand up satisfactorily to service conditions and to have sufficient flexibility to prevent cracking having regard to the working of the ship at sea.

2.8 Suitability under varying climatic conditions

The materials are required to remain in satisfactory and serviceable condition over the range of temperatures experienced in service whether Arctic, Temperate, or Tropical.

2.9 Corrosion

A deck covering should preferably not contain any substance which may have a corrosive effect on the metal deck, but where such substances are present a suitable protective coating is to be applied to the deck before the covering is laid.

2.10 Adhesion

A covering should be capable of being laid on a clean metal deck and should adhere effectively to the deck, either by itself or by the use of a suitable adhesive.

2.11 Oil resistance

2.11.1 General
   .1.1 Where the floors of crew accommodation are also the crowns of oil fuel tanks the coverings are to be tested for oil resistance.
   .1.2 Oil resisting compound laid in way of the crown of oil tanks shall be at least 1.5 mm in thickness. Also it will be necessary to ensure that it does not suffer appreciably at the temperatures likely to be experienced in service in the case of heated tanks. This compound, if of a suitable nature may also form the adhesive for securing the covering to the underside of decks. See para 4.
   .1.3 Coatings and adhesives used as primer or for securing materials direct to crowns of oil tanks are also to be tested.
2.11.2 Method of Testing
   .2.1 A test sample of 300 mm × 300 mm and of the thickness proposed to be used is to be weighed and then immersed in fuel oil maintained at a temperature of 66 degrees Centigrade for 24 hours. It is then to be carefully cleaned and weighed again. The sample should be broken up to the amount of oil penetration to be measured, penetration should be such as to be classed as 'not appreciable' i.e. less than 1 mm.

2.12 Other Tests

Other tests in addition to these stated above may be required depending on the nature of the covering material.

3. Coverings for the floors of crew accommodation

3.1 General

.1.1 All finished deck coverings should be approved by the Department and be laid on similarly approved underlays.

.1.2 Underlays should present a flush upper surface and should not be less than 6.5 mm in thickness in crew sleeping rooms and 8.0 mm in all other crew spaces. Where there are deformities in the upper surface of the deck plating these thicknesses stated, which are a minimum, will need to be increased.

.1.3 Materials such as vinyl sheeting or tiles may be used as the finished covering in these spaces.

.1.4 Finished coverings should not in general be less than 2 mm in thickness and should adequately adhere to the underlay. Proposals to use a finished deck covering of thickness less than 2 mm will be considered on merit.

.1.5 Adhesive used to bond finished coverings to underlays should be insoluble in water. If the adhesive is of a type which gives off vapour while being used, it should be ensured that all necessary precautions are taken against the risks.

.1.6 Trowel laid coverings for underlays or for combined underlays and finished coverings may be used. Examples of this type of coverings are those based on rubber latex, or synthetic resins, mixed with cement, sand and various other fillers. Full particulars of such materials should be submitted for consideration.

.1.7 In the case of coverings of the magnesium oxychloride type an anti-corrosive coating at least 6 mm in thickness is to be first applied so as to cover completely the metal deck to protect the plating against possible corrosive action. Such coatings are to be of types accepted by the Department.

.1.8 All coverings in crew accommodation should be rounded up where the floor meets the boundary bulkhead.

.1.9 Except in the case of underlays of magnesium oxychloride type, or where the deck forms the crown of an oil fuel tank, formal acceptance by the Department is not required for anti-corrosives and adhesives which are not now included in the Department's list of accepted covering. Surveyors should be satisfied that such materials and their application are satisfactory.

4. Coverings on the underside of weather decks which are crowns of crew accommodation

4.1 General

.1.1 The material should be applied to the deck so as to avoid harbourage for dirt and vermin but consideration will be given to proposals to apply the material to the topside of ceilings. In all cases consideration should be given to the fitting of a vapour barrier fitted to the exposed surface of the material to prevent condensation as far as may be practicable.

.1.2 Particulars of the method of fixings the material should be submitted for approval.

5. Decks exposed to appreciable heat or cold

5.1 General

.1.1 These decks include those in way of machinery spaces galleys, heated oil tanks, refrigerated spaces, etc.

.1.2 Floors of crew accommodation which are exposed to appreciable heat or cold on the underside are to be suitably insulated. Unless adequate insulation is fitted on the underside suitable insulating material should, in general, be fitted on the deck and then covered with an accepted deck covering.

6. Floors of hospitals and similar spaces

6.1 General

.1.1 Floors of such spaces are required to comply, in general, with the requirements specified in paragraph 3. They are to have a smooth but not slippery surface which can easily be kept clean. The number of joints in the covering should be kept to a minimum and hence vinyl tiles or other suitable materials in tile form will not be accepted.

.1.2 A cove should be formed at the boundaries. The material should be such that it will not be damaged by surgical spirit or other liquids which may be expected to be used in such spaces.

.1.3 Vinyl sheeting firmly adhered to an acceptable underlay is recommended as a suitable flooring in hospital wards and similar.

7. Floors of bathroom, washplaces, water closets and similar spaces

7.1 General

.1.1 Floors of these spaces should be covered with ceramic tiles or other similar coverings. The tiles should be laid in cement or other suitable underlay and coved at the boundaries.

.1.2 It is recommended that the floors of these spaces be light in colour.

.1.3   Particular attention should be given to foothold character-
       istics under wet conditions.

.1.4   Where a sleeping room has a semi-private or private
       bathroom the same type of flooring used for the sleeping
       room may, if desired, be fitted in the bathroom.

Appendix A

(Reproduced from Appendix X in 'Fire Protection Instructions')

ACCEPTANCE OF DECK COVERINGS FOR USE IN ACCOMMO-
DATION SPACES, SERVICE SPACES AND CONTROL STATIONS
ON UNITED KINGDOM REGISTERED SHIPS

REQUIREMENTS RELATING TO IGNITABILITY, TOXICITY AND
EXPLOSIVE HAZARDS

1.   THE MERCHANT SHIPPING (CREW ACCOMMODATION)
REGULATIONS 1978

1.1   Item (3) of Schedule 1 to the Merchant Shipping (Crew Accommodation) Regulations 1978 requires a deck covering which is laid on decks
in crew accommodation on United Kingdom registered ships to be such
that it will not readily ignite.

1.2   In order that the Department may be satisfied that a deck covering
complies with this requirement, samples of the material are required to
be subjected to the test specified in paragraph 3 below and are to satisfy
the pass criteria.

1.3   The test may be carried out by any recognised testing laboratory
independent of the manufacturer of the deck covering or constituent
materials.

1.4   A copy of the test report issued by the testing laboratory is required
to be submitted to the Department for consideration. If the report is
not in English then an English translation should accompany the report.
The report is required to give full details of each constituent material of
the deck covering including its thickness.

1.5   Compliance with the other requirements of Schedule 1 is the subject
of separate information supplied by the Crew Accommodation Branch
of the Department.

2.   THE MERCHANT SHIPPING (FIRE PROTECTION) REGU-
LATIONS 1984

2.1   Regulations 84(2)(d), 100(2)(d), 121(2) and 138(2) of the Merchant
Shipping (Fire Protection) Regulations 1984 require primary deck coverings in accommodation and service spaces and control stations to be of
an approved material which will not readily ignite or give rise to toxic
or explosive hazards at elevated temperatures.

2.2   For the purpose of these Regulations a primary deck covering is
to be regarded as the first layer of a floor construction which is applied
directly on top of the deck plating and is inclusive of any priming coat,
anti-corrosive compound or adhesive which is necessary to provide
protection or adhesion to the deck plating.

2.3   Although there are existing testing procedures by which toxicity
and explosive hazards may be quantified there are no pass/fail criteria
specified. These items are currently under discussion at the International
Maritime Organisation (IMO) and it is hoped that the situation will be
resolved in the not too distant future. Manufacturers will be informed

when testing procedures and pass/fail criteria have been adopted by IMO and discussions will take place with industry before such procedures and criteria are implemented by the Department.

In the meantime the Department will only require primary deck coverings to be tested as indicated in section 1 of this information sheet.

3. IGNITABILITY TEST FOR DECK COVERINGS WHICH ARE TO BE USED ON UNITED KINGDOM REGISTERED SHIPS

3.1 TEST SPECIMENS

3.1.1 Three specimens of the deck covering are to be prepared.

3.1.2 The specimens are to be a minimum of 150 mm × 150 mm and of the thickness which is to be used on board ships and attached to 3 mm thick steel plating.

3.2 CONDITIONING OF TEST SPECIMENS

3.2.1 The conditioning atmosphere shall have a temperature of $20 \pm 2°C$ and relative humidity of $65 \pm 2\%$.

3.2.2 The specimens shall be laid flat, singly and with the steel plating on the underside in the conditioning atmosphere for a period of 24 hours, or for a sufficiently longer period in order to ensure that the mass of each specimen shows no progressive change greater than 0.25% when it is determined at intervals of 2 hours.

3.3 ATMOSPHERE FOR TESTING

3.3.1 The test is to be conducted in the same atmosphere as for conditioning the specimens, or within 2 minutes of removal from the conditioning atmosphere.

3.3.2 Appropriate measures should be taken to prevent draughts in the vicinity of the testing equipment when testing is in progress.

3.4 TESTING PROCEDURE

3.4.1 Source of ignition

The source shall be obtained by using a burner consisting of a copper tube having a length of 150 mm and inside and outside diameters of 5 mm and 6 mm respectively connected by plastic or rubber tubing to a gas tap supplying natural gas. The copper tube is to have no opening for the supply of air.

3.4.2 Height of flame

Before the test takes place the burner flame is to be adjusted to a height of 32 mm.

3.4.3 Test procedure

3.4.3.1 Place a specimen horizontally on a metal tripod stand with the upper surface of the specimen facing downwards (i.e. with steel plating uppermost) such that the height of this surface of the specimen is approximately 8 mm below the top of the burner flame. Apply the burner flame at right angles to the plane of the specimen in the centre of the specimen. After one minute the burner flame is to be removed clear of the specimen and the time in seconds to extinction of any flaming is to be recorded.

3.4.3.2   The test in paragraph 3.4.3.1 is to be repeated after any flaming or smouldering has ceased and the temperature of the specimen has returned to normal except that the centre of the burner flame is to be positioned at the same height at the midpoint of any edge of the specimen. Again the time in seconds to extinction of any flaming after the removal of the burner is to be recorded.

3.4.3.3   The tests in paragraphs 3.4.3.1 and 3.4.3.2 are to be carried out on the two remaining specimens and the times to extinction of any flaming recorded.

3.5   PASS CRITERIA

A deck covering is deemed to be 'not readily ignitable' when the flaming of the test specimens ceases within 20 seconds of the removal of the burner flame.

Appendix B

APPROVED FLOORINGS AND UNDERLAYS IN CREW AND PASSENGER ACCOMMODATION

Name and Address of Manufacturer	Name of Material	MDM No	Official Ref	Approval Expiry Date
A B Strangbetong ltd Box 20 524 00 Herrijunga Sweden	S-floor element 655 types 81 and 81 insulated deck coverings		MC25/8/0271	1.1.1955
Altro Limited Caxton Hill Hertford SG13 7NB	Altro Safety Flooring Altro Safety Flooring/Glass Fibre Reinforcement including Type T20 Mondopave Studded Rubber Mipolam 2mm	133/77 135/78 191/78	CM20171/52 CM20171/52 CM20171/52 MC25/8/094	1.1.1995 1.1.1995 1.1.1995 1.1.1955
A Michaelski & Cia Ltd Rua Vivva Claudio, 291 Rio de Janeiro Brazil	Pisnai Pisnave 1/Termolite 650 Insulated Deck Covering	362/81	MC25/8/0126	1.1.1995
Amtico	Amtico Wood Collection floor material (Different Print Finish)	300/86	MC25/8/0282	7.1996
API Spa	Amtico VR4 Tiles Flexisecurit ER	233/86 217/86	MC25/8/0282 MC25/8/0280	25.3.1996 5.3.1996
Ardex UK Ltd Homefield Road Haverhill Suffolk CB9 8QP	Ardex latex under-layment Ardex Primary Deck Covering	156/78 282/85	MC25/8/0203 MC25/8/0267	1.1.1995
Armstrong House 3 Chequers Square Uxbridge Middlesex UB8 1NG	Textelle 125 Designer Solarian Accoflex Rhino Contract Flooring	371/83 255/85 284/85 395/85	MC25/8/0258 MC25/8/0258 MC25/8/0258 MC25/8/0258	1.1.1995 28.3.1995 6.6.1995 25.11.95
ASK Corporation 10-6-7 Chome Ginza Chuo-Ku Tokyo-104 Japan	Marlite SR-F Floor	332/84 336/87	MC25/8/0270	1.1.1995
Boldt Kunstafftoepassing BV Edisonweg 14 Postbus 55 2950 AB Alblasserdam Holland	Boliscreed PU/SL Boliscreed PU/SL D60	242/86 243/86	MC25/8/0281 MC25/8/0281	4.1996 4.1996
Cape Boards and panels Ltd Germiston Works Petershill Road Glasgow G21 4AU	Cape Marine Floor (A60 rating)		MC25/8/0220	1.1.1995
Carl Freudenberg & Co Ltd Lutterworth Leicestershire LE17 4DU	Norament 923 Studded Rubber		MC25/8/0257	1.1.1995

Name and Address of Manufacturer	Name of Material	MDM No	Official Ref	Approval Expiry Date
Colas Building Products Ltd Riverside Saltrey Chester CH4 8RS	Flooring Emulsion Mastic Flooring Laybond latex smoothing compound		MC25/8/027	1.1.1995
Datwyler AG Schwizerische Kabel Gummiund Kunststoffwerke CH–6460 Altdorf	Toro Elastic flooring Toro flooring Select Super flooring	344/85	MC25/8/0266	1.1.1995
Davidson SPA PO Box 1927 16100 Genoa Italy	Navilastic Navilastic H T-Roxby Marine Deck	206/86	MC25/8/0127 MC25/8/0127 MC25/8/0127	1.1.1995 3.1.1996
Dex-O-Tex International Ltd 15 Bleinhelm Road Cressex Industrial Estate High Wycombe Bucks HP12 3RS	Dex-O-Tex Neotex 28 Deck Covering Dex-O-Tex Neotex P–67 Deck Covering Deck-O-Tex Subkote No 2 Underlay	196/78 197/78 198/78	MC25/8/0213	1.1.1995 1.1.1995 1.1.1995
DLW Aktiengesell-schaft Postfach 140 7120 Bietigheim-Bissingen West Germany or West Way House Elms Parade Oxford OX2 9LL	Deliplan Royal		MC25/8/093	1.1.1995
Dunloplan Division Dunlop AG Semtex-Schiffbau Weidenbaumsweg 107 2050 Hamburg 80 Federal Republic of Germany	Semtex SX 547L Semtex 547A SX-PG 30/40 Insulated SX-SP/TR 30/40 insulated SX-FKA 30/20R insulated	236/86 235/86 234/86	MC25/8/0196 MC25/8/0196 MC25/8/0196 MC25/8/0196	1.1.1995 1.1.1995 26.3.1996 26.3.1996 26.3.1996
Durastic Limited Victoria Works 306 Burdett Road London E14 7DH	Durastic Insulated Decking Type 300 Durastic Solasdek (A60) Decking Type CA Durastic Solasdek (A60) Decking Type PE Durastic Combination Flooring Durastic Insulphat Underlay Durastic Cold Lay Flooring Durastic Cold Lay Underlay Granodek Durastic S473 Composition Durstic Solasdek Type PE insulated Deck Sheathing	 186/78 165/75	MC25/8/0172 MC25/8/0172 MC25/8/0172 CM23806/30 CM23806/30 CM20138/48 CM20138/48 CM20138/48 MS47/10/046 MC25/8/0172 Pt 1	1.1.1995 1.1.1995 1.1.1995 1.1.1995 1.1.1995 1.1.1995 1.1.1995 1.1.1995 1.1.1995 1.1.1995
Durastic Limited Victoria Road 306 Burdett Road London E14 7DH	Durastic Solasdek Type RW insulated Deck Sheathing Durastic Solasdek Type CA insulated Deck Sheathing Durastic Sound Reducing Decking type RW	164/75 166/75 141/77	MC25/8/0172 Pt 1 MC25/8/0172 Pt 1 MC25/8/0168	1.1.1995 1.1.1995

90

Name and Address of Manufacturer	Name of Material	MDM No	Official Ref	Approval Expiry Date
	Durastic internal insulated Decking type 300	146/77	MC25/8/0181	1.1.1995
	Durastic internal insulated Decking Type S412		MC25/8/0181	1.1.1995
	Durastic Accodek Solasdek (A60) RW		MC25/8/0172	1.1.1995
	Durastic Thermal insulated Deck Sheathing	38/75	MC25/8/022	1.1.1995
	Durastic Accodek LA Composition	72/74	MC25/8/022	1.1.1995
	Durastic Accodek UA Granite Filled	72/74	MC25/8/022	1.1.1995
	Durastic Accodek UA Cork Filled	72/74	MC25/8/022	1.1.1995
	Durastic Accodek KA Granite Filled	72/74	MC25/8/022	1.1.1995
	Durastic Accodek KA Cork Filled	72/74	MC25/8/022	1.1.1995
	Durastic Accodek PRA Granite Filled	72/74	MC25/8/022	1.1.1995
	Durastic Accodek PRA Cork Filled	72/74	MC25/8/022	1.1.1995
	Durastic Accodek UBA Cork Filled	72/74	MC25/8/022	1.1.1995
	Durastic Accodek NS Granite Filled	72/74	MC25/8/022	1.1.1995
	Durastic Accodek EI Composition		MC25/8/041	1.1.1995
	Durastic HT Underlay			
	Durastic Dekoprene Cold Lay		MS47/10/050	1.1.1995
	Durastic Dekoprene Underlay		MS47/10/047	1.1.1995
	Durastic Cold Lay Mk2 Type Underlay	145/79	MC25/8/069	1.1.1995
	Durastic Cold Lay Mk2 Type FG Underlay	146/79	MC25/8/069	1.1.1995
	*Duravin internal Deck Covering		CM20138/48	1.1.1995
	Durastic Latex Underlay		MS47/10/046	1.1.1995
	Durastic Sound Reducing Decking		MC25/8/0168	1.1.1995
	Durastic Dekoradek Epoxy Flooring	385/87	MC25/9/0556	14.12.97
	Durastic S776 Epoxy Flooring		MC25/9/0556	14.12.98
	Durastic S450 Epoxy Flooring		MC25/9/0556	14.12.97
	Durastic S405 Epoxy Compound Type FR	269/88	MC25/9/0556	5.5.98
	Durastic Extralite underlay S800	273/88	MC25/9/0560	5.5.98
S229/S346 S222/S345	Durastic Sound Reducing Decking Type RWHT & RWCL		MC25/8/0168	1.1.1995
	Unidese (non accommodation spaces)		MC25/8/0280	1.1.1995
	Durastic Solasdek insulated Deck Covering Type Grandek (Reinforced)	271/81	MC25/8/0172	1.1.1995
			MC25/8/0172	1.11.1995
	Durastic Solasdek A60 Decking	373/85		
	Type RWHT (Reinforced) insulated Deck Sheathing	349/81	MC25/8/0172	1.1.1995
			MC25/8/0172	9.1.1996
	Durastic Solasdek A60 Deck Type Grandek (Reinforced)	205/86		

Name and Address of Manufacturer	Name of Material	MDM No	Official Ref	Approval Expiry Date
Forbo-Nairn Ltd	Armourflex	342/86	MC25/8/0283	29.1.1997
PO Box No 1	Armourflor	262/87	MC25/8/0283	1.4.1997
Kirkcaldy	Sureslep 263/87	262/87		1.4.1997
Fife	Marmoleum Marbled			
KY1 2SB	linoleum	217/88	MC25/8/0283	1.2.1998
Scotland	Krommenie Plain Linoleum			
	Linoflex Linoleum Tiles			
Fagertun-Tarkett AS	Favoritt/D-Cover		MC25/8/0130	1.1.1995
PO Box 453				
N-3001 Drammen				
Norway				
Forbo-Krommenie (UK)	Smaragd 2.0		MC25/8/0256	1.1.1995
Ltd				
Leet Court				
14 King Street				
Watford				
Herts				
WD1 7AD				
Franchi Wood Mosaic	Fran-Kee MCP Sheathing	383/67	CM21604/1952	1.1.1995
Co Ltd	Fran-Kee Granesco Flooring	MDM 7045	CM/1962	
London				
N8 8PR				
Gerland Limited	Gerflex Classic Vinyl		MC25/8/061	1.1.1995
90 Crawford Street	Gerflex Architectron Tiles	89/64		
London				
1H 2AP				
G Theodor Freese	Tefrotex 25/5 "L" underlay			1.1.1995
Schongaver Strasse 7	Tefrotex 25/5 underlay		MC25/8/087	1.1.1995
28 Bremen 15	Tefrotex Type 60 Levelite			1.1.1995
West Germany	Tefrotex 25/5 "ILU" with 6TF Block		MC25/8/0128	1.1.1995
	Tefrotex B		MC47/3/0312	1.1.1995
	Tefroka PU-1 and Tefroka PU-1 Marine/Navy (No objection issued 28/9/87)		MC25/8/287	
Harefield Rubber	Special Harefield Rubber	252/84	MC25/8/0424	1.1.1995
Company Ltd	Flooring			
Bell Works				
Harefield				
Middlesex				
WB9 6HG				
James Halstead Ltd	Polytred		MC25/8/088	1.1.1995
PO Box 3	Polyflor XL	184/79	MC25/8/0157	1.1.1995
Radcliff New Road	Gameflor		MC25/8/0244	1.1.1995
Whitefield	Polytred dB/XL	185/79	MC25/8/0157	1.1.1995
Manchester	Polyflor Super XL	285/85	MC25/8/0157	14.6.1995
M25 7NR	Polysafe Decortile	286/85	MC25/8/0157	14.6.1995
	Polysafe PVC	293/84	MC25/8/0157	1.1.1995
James Walker & Co Ltd	Treadmaster FR matting		MC25/8/045	
Lion Works				
Woking				
Surrey				
GU22 8AP				
K E Marine Floor	Ardex Primary Deck	282/85	MC25/8/0267	5.6.1995
Systems	Covering System			

Name and Address of Manufacturer	Name of Material	MDM No	Official Ref	Approval Expiry Date
Kobe Tought Kosan & Co Ltd 664–2 Matsunouchi Junna Ikawadani-Cho Tarumi-Ku Kobe Japan	High-Tex underlay	230/78	MC25/8/0195	1.1.1995
Kuriyama Rubber Co Ltd No 12–4, 1 Chome Nishinakajima Yodogawa-Ku Osaka Japan	Matico S Fresh Lontile Lonleum	283/81 206/81 205/81	MC25/8/0156	1.1.1995 1.1.1995 1.1.1995
Lamacrest Ltd Crown Works Harrogate HG2 0NR Yorks	Lamacrest Fire Retardant Lightweight Epoxy Underlay	316/81	MC25/8/0228	1.1.1995
Lucky Ltd	Marble Mat PVC Flooring	375/85	MC25/8/0263	30.10.95
Marieholms Industrie AB 400 13 Goteborg Sweden	Miab Litosilo Floating Floor System with Miab Variants & with Litosilo Primer Miab Coloured Variants Structam Variant Epoxy Resins		MC25/8/0170 MC25/8/0170 MC25/8/0170	1.1.1995 1.1.1995 1.1.1995
Marley Floors Limited Lenham Maidstone Kent ME17 2DE	HD Series 2 Marley Econoflex Tiles HD Safetred New Formula Format	229/80 305/88	MC25/8/086 MC25/8/086 MC25/8/086 MC25/9/0572	1.1.1995 1.1.1995 1.1.1995 1998
Nichias Corporation 1–2 Shibadalmon 1–Chome Minato-Ku tokyo 105 Japan	Rockmarine Floating Floor	201/86	MC25/8/247	9.1.1996
Nordsovaerftet 6050 Ringkobing Denmark	Nordsovaerftet Floating Floor	239/80 212/81	MC25/9/0368	1.1.1995
Oy Stockfors AB SF 07901 Lovisa Finland	Stockfors Floating Floor		MC25/8/0261	1.1.1995
Pegulan Limited 105 Devonshire Road London W4 2HU	Elastic Super	349/68	MC25/8/0111	1.1.1995
Perogen Espan SA Matin Machio 12 Madrid 2 Spain	Navaltex Underlay		MC25/8/063	1.1.1995
Perstorp AB S-28400 Perstorp Sweden	Perginol Standard SR Perginol Industry Perginol Anti-Skid Peran STB: 5	340/85 304/86	MC25/8/0163 MC25/8/0163 MC25/8/0259 MC25/8/0259	1.1.1995 1.1.1995 3.9.1995 8.1996

Name and Address of Manufacturer	Name of Material	MDM No	Official Ref	Approval Expiry Date
Rieber & Sons Ltd California Drive	Rickett PVC Floor Tiles	377/85	MC25/9/0146	1.11.1995
Roberts Smoothedge Ltd	Renda-Flor L3/Latex/ Cement underlay (Super & Standard)		MC25/8/0122	1.1.1995
Rowan and Boden (Contracts) Ltd 1 Edison Street Hillington Glasgow	Aranbee Underlay Comp U3	No 9839	MC25/8/034	1.1.1995
	Aranbee RB731 Epoxy Resin Comp	142/64	MC25/8/062	1.1.1995
	Aranbee Lightweight Deck Screed	247/88	MC25/8/062	17.3.98
Samgong Co Ltd 948-2 Kamjon-Dong Buk-Ku, Busan Korea	Samgong Tightex 307A	354/82	MC25/8/0245	1.1.1995
	Samgong Tightex 309A	355/82		
Scanvi A/S Prinsensgt Oslo Norway	Halbacc Floating Floor	302/81	MC25/8/0229	1.1.1995
Signal Marine Units 25-27 Galgate Mill Lancaster	Featherdeck	263/85	MC25/8/0275	10.10.95
	Trawlerdeck	264/85	MC25/8/0231	10.10.95
	Featherdeck Trawlerdeck Combined Sandwich	401/85	MC25/8/0231	3.12.1995
	Featherdeck 70	345/87	MC25/8/0289	9.10.1997
SIRN sri Via del Lazzaretto Vecchio 9 34123 Trieste Italy	Dunlop Semtex SX 547B	255/80	CM20073/44	1.1.1995
	Dunlop Semtex SX 530C			1.1.1995
	Semprene lightweight			1.1.1995
	Semprene Terrazo			1.1.1995
Sumitomo Rubber Industries Ltd 1-1 Tsutsai-Cho 1-Chome Fukai-Ku PO Box 345 Kobe Port Kobe, 651-01 Japan	Dunlop Semtex SX 547B	254/80	MC25/8/0188	
	Dunlop Semtex SX 530C		MC25/8/0188	
	Semprene Terrazzo			
	PV 154V			
	SX 547-B-F Floating Floor			
Swedish Acoustic Products	Swedac Deck Covering System VI	317/82	MC25/8/0225	1.1.1995
Innovations AB Hildedalsgatan 26A	Swedac SBR-latex concrete	204/85	MC25/8/0225	1.1.1995
S-417 05 Gothenburg Sweden	Swedac Deck Covering System V2	382/85	MC25/8/0225	1.1.1995
Taihei Kogyo Co Ltd Sanjodori-Nishioshi- Nishi Ukyo-Ku Kyoto 615 Japan	Tightex 305A, 307A, 309A on New Taikalite Marine Board		MC25/8/0113	1.1.1995
Takara Kensai Seisakusho Co Ltd 3-14 Hanamote-Cho Atsuta-Ku Nagoya Japan	Uniex-SA		MC25/8/ 0264	1.1.1995

Name and Address of Manufacturer	Name of Material	MDM No	Official Ref	Approval Expiry Date
Takiron Co Ltd Yasutomi Factory 405 Totaguchi Nagano, Yasutomi-Cho Shisou-Gun Hyogo Pref Japan	Takistlon Vinyl Sheet Flooring	276/88	MC25/9/0567	17.5.88
Texmar International AB S–434 02 Kungsback Sweden	Texmar M19 with N without VG damping	261/88	MC25/9/0542	25.4.1998
Veitchi (Scotland) Ltd 15 Bouverie Street Rutherglen Glasgow G73 2RY	Veitchi Plasdex Flexoleum		CM21703/37 CM20754/40 CM21703/37	1.1.1995 1.1.1995 1.1.1995
Waile Dove Bitumastic PLC Hedgeley Road Hebburn Tyne & Wear NE31 1EY	"Bitumastic" Granite Filled Underlay "Bitumastic" Cork-Filled Underlay	259/88 304/88	MC25/8/0277 MC25/8/0277	11.4.98 19.7.98
Whitemore-Northway (Holdings) Ltd Church Street Frodsham Warrington Lancs WA6 7DP	Dekotread Heavy Duty Flooring Beldamat		MC25/8/0215	1.1.1995
W H Keys Ltd Hall End Works Church Lane West Bromwich B71 1BN	Mastico		1.1.1995	
Yatomi Shokai Co Ltd 113 Minamisengen-Cho Nishi-Ku Yokohama Japan	Yatomix NS Floor HD Type, LD Type, EC Type		MC25/8/0146	1.1.1995

Appendix C

APPROVED COVERINGS FOR THE UNDERSIDE OF WEATHER DECKS FORMING THE CROWNS OF CREW AND PASSENGER ACCOMMODATION

Name and Address of Manufacturer	Name of Material	MDM No	Official Ref	Expiry Date
ASK Corporation 10–6, 7 Chome Ginza Chuo-Ku, Tokyo 104 Japan	Ask Glass Felt 16 kg Glass Fibre Insulation Ask Rock Fire board	180/78	MC25/9/0306	1.1.1996
	No 80 Mineral Wool Insulation density 80 kg/m³	181/78	MC25/9/0306	1.1.1996
	Ask Rock Fire Board No 40 Insulation faced with Aluminium foil, density 40 kg/m³	195/79	MC25/9/0306	1.1.1996
	Ask High Heat Board-G	203/86 336/87	MC25/9/0306	3.1.1996
Asahi Fiber Class Co Ltd PO Box 5019 Shinjuku Daiichi Seimei Building Shinjuku-Ku, Tokyo Japan	Glasron Wool GW310 insulation (density 20 kg/k³)	367/81	MC25/9/0308	1.1.1996
	Glasron Wool GW312 (density 24 kg/m³)		MC25/9/0308	1.1.1996
	Glasron Wool GW416 (density 32 kg/m³)		MC25/9/0308	1.1.1996
	Glasron wool GW310-AL		MC25/9/0308	1.1.1996
	Glasron wool GW312-AL		MC25/9/0308	1.1.1996
	Glasron wool GW416-AL		MC25/9/0308	1.1.1996
Companhia Vidraria Santa Marina Avenida Santa Marina 42 CP 2931 Sao Paulo SP Brazil	PAT-N Glass Fibre Insulation (density 60 kg/m³ ± 10%)	292/81	MC25/9/0402	1.1.1996
Deutsche Rockwool Mineralwall GmbH 139 Gladbeck Postfach 207 Bottroper Strasse 241 West Germany	Rockwool Dammplatten RP/III (density 30 kg/m³)		MC25/8/0116	1.1.1996
	Rockwool Dammplatten RP/V (density 50 kg/m³)		MS47/3/0202	1.1.1996
	Rockwool Dammplatten PR/VII (density 70 kg/m³)			
Fiberglas Canada Ltd 3080 Yonge Street Toronto Ontario Canada M4N 3NI	Fiberglas TW-MC Insulation	145/77	MC25/8/0168	1.1.1996
Grunzweig & Harttmann und Glasfaser AG 6700 Ludwigshafenfam Rhein	Isover Mineral Fibre Mats MDD/TR Isover Mineral Fibre Slabs ST/TR (density 100–200 kg/m³)		MC25/8/0109	1.1.1996
	Isover Mineral Fibre Slabs SP/TRS		MC25/8/0109	1.1.1996
	Silan SF43		MC25/8/0109	1.1.1996
	Silan SF39		MC25/8/0109	1.1.1996
	Isover Mineral Fibre Slabs Sillatherm TR Isover File (density 20 kg/ m³)		MC25/8/0109	1.1.1996
		208/79	MS47/3/0180	1.1.1996
	Isover/Platherm Mineral Wool (density 20 kg/m³)	208/79	MS47/3/0180	1.1.1996

Name and Address of Manufacturer	Name of Material	MDM No	Official Ref	Approval Expiry Date
Nichias Corporation No 1–26, 1-Chome Shiba Baimon Minato-Ku Tokyo 105 Japan	MGB Felt Mineral Wool Insulation (density 60 kg/m³ ± 10%)	227/78	MC25/9/0324	1.1.1996
The Nippon Muki Co Ltd Ohm Building 3–1, Kanda-Nishikicho Chiyoda-Ku Tokyo Japan	Superfine SPF-216 and SPF-200 CF-18 Glass Fibre Insulation (density 16 and 20 kg/m³ ± 10% respectively)		MC25/9/0424	1.1.1996
Pilkington Fibreglass Ltd Insulation Division St Helens Merseyside WA10 3TR	Rocksil AF16, AF20, AF32 & AF48 Mineral Wool Insulation (densities 16, 20, 32 & 48 kg/m³ respectively)	143/77	MS47/10/031	1.1.1996
	Rocksil 16/20 Building Slabs (density 16–20 kg/m³)		MS47/10/031	1.1.1996
	Rocksil Resin Bonded Slabs LR32 & LR48 (densities 32 and 48 kg/m³ respectively)		MS47/10/031	1.1.1996
	Rocksil VF16, VF20, VF32 & VF48 (densities 16, 20, 32 & 48 kg/m³ respectively)	142/77	MS47/10/031	1.1.1996
	Rocksil Mineral Fibre Marine Board (density 48 kg/m³)		MS47/10/031	1.1.1996
	Superfine 'B' Fibre Navy Board Crown 100, Crown 200 Crown 100HT		MS47/10/09	1.1.1996
Rockwool AB Fack 615 S–541–86 Skorde Sweden	Ecomax Slab 331 Mineral Wool Insulation (density 40 kg/m³)	234/77	MC25/9/0325	1.1.1996
	Ecomax Slab 335 Mineral Wool Insulation (density 100 kg/m³)	134/78	MC25/9/0325	1.1.1996
	Ecomax Slab 333 Mineral Wool Insulation (density 65 kg/m³ ± 10%)	379/81	MC25/9/0325	1.1.1996
	Ecomax 1131–00 Mineral Wool Insulation (density 30 kg/m³ ± 10%)		MC25/9/0325	1.1.1996
Rockwool A/S DK 2640 Hedehusene Denmark	Rockwool Marine Batts 30 Mineral Wool Insulation (density 30 kg/m³)		MC25/9/093	1.1.1996
	Rockwool Marine Batts 40 Insulation (density 40 kg/m³)		MC25/9/093	1.1.1996
	Rockwool Marine Batts 45 Insulation (density 45 kg/m³)		MC25/9/093	1.1.1996
Rockwool Lapinus BV Industrieweg 15 6074 NH Melick-Herkenbosch Postbus 1180 6040 Ko Roemond Netherlands	Rockwool Insulation Slab Type 223 Mineral Wool Insulation (density 100 ± 10% kg/m³)			1.1.1996

Name and Address of Manufacturer	Name of Material	MDM No	Official Ref	Approval Expiry Date
Rockwool Ltd Pencoed Bridgend Mid Glamorgan CF35 6NY	Rockwool Slab Type RW3, RW4 and RW5 Mineral Wool Insulation (densities 60 + 10% kg/m^3, 80 $\pm$ 10% kg/m^3 and 100 $\pm$ 10% kg/m^3 respectively)		MC25/9/0425	1.1.1996
	Rockwool RW2 Slab Rockwool RWAY5 Slab Mineral Wool insulations (density 33 kg/m^3 $\pm$ 10%, 45 kg/m^3 $\pm$ 10% respectively)		MC25/9/0425	1.1.1996

Appendix D

APPROVED COVERINGS FOR THE TOPSIDE OF WEATHER DECKS FORMING THE CROWNS OF CREW ACCOMMODATION

Name and Address of Manufacturer	Name of Material	MDM No	Official Ref	Expiry Date
Cape Insulation Ltd Stirling Scotland FK7 7RW	Rocksil Bonded Slabs		MS47/10/031	
Dunlop Semtex Ltd Brynmawr Gwent NP3 4XN	*Girpdec *Semprene Lightweight Weather Decking *Semtex Epoxy Terrazzo Decking		MC25/8/076 MC25/8/096 MC25/8/0124	
Durastic Limited Victoria Works Burdett Road London	Durastic Weather Deck Sheathing Durastic Insulphalt Weather Deck Sheathing Durastic Accodeck Weather Deck Sheathing Type LC & LCI Durastic Dekoprene Weather Deck Sheathing Type WG Durastic Dekoprene Weather Deck Sheathing Type LCI Durastic Accodek Insulated Deck Sheathing *Durastic Accodeck Epoxy Surfacing Composition		CM20138/48 MC25/8/069 MS47/10/046 MS47/10/046 MS47/10/046 MC25/8/039 MC25/8/077	
Franchi-Wood Mosaic Co Ltd 4 Topsfield Parade London N8 8PR	*Fran-Kee MCP Sheathing		CM21604/52	
Ludwig Ditmers GmbH Witternstrasse 2 Postfach 93 0660 2102 Hamburg 93	Tenuxon Outside Deck Covering T 402	48/72	MC25/8/0110	
Perogen Espanola SA Martin Machio 12 Madrid 2 Spain	*Deckatex R		MC25/8/063	
Rowan & Boden (Contracts) Ltd 1 Edison Street Glasgow G52 4UF	Airadek Neodek		MS47/10/027 MS47/10/027	
Societe Impianti Riparazioni Navali Per Axioni Cicerone 10 Trieste Italy	Semprene Lightweight Weather Decking		CM20073/44	

* in conjunction with an approved type underdeck insulation

Name and Address of Manufacturer	Name of Material	MDM No	Official Ref	Approval Expiry Date
Sumitomo Rubber Industries Ltd 1–1 Tsutsai-Cho 1-Chome Fukai-ku PO Box 345 Kobe Port Kobe, 651–01 Japan	Semprene Lightweight Weather Decking		MC25/8/0188	
Veitchi (Scotland) Ltd 15 Bouverie Street Rutherglen Glasgow G73 2RY	Plasdek		CM20754/40	
Yatomi Shokai Co 21–1 Minamisengen- Cho Nishi-Ku Yokohama Japan	*Yatomix Ex-Deck *Yatomix NS Floor (HD, LD & EC types)		MC25/8/0148	

* in conjunction with an approved type underdeck insulation

Appendix E

APPROVED COATINGS FOR USE UNDER DECK COVERINGS OF THE MAGNESIUM OXYCHLORIDE TYPE OR UNDER DECK COVERINGS ON THE CROWNS OF FUEL OIL TANKS

Name and Address of Manufacturer	Name of Material	Official Reference No.
Dunlop Semtex Ltd Brynmawr, Gwent, NP3 4XN	Semcoat Semtex P.V.154 Semtex P.V > 154B Bitumastic Oil resistant Priming Solution	CM.20212/42 CM.20212/42 CM.20073/44 CM.21041/40
Durastic Ltd Victoria Works, Burdett Road, London E14	Durip Oil Resisting Compound Durip Anti-Slip Oil Resisting Compound	CM.22849/49 CM.22849/49
Wailes Dove Bitumastic Ltd Darlington Road, Shieldon, Co Durham	Bitumastic Oil Resistant Solution	CM.21041/40

ANNEX 3

Thermostatic Shower Mixing Valves
SCHEDULE OF TESTS

This Annex outlines the procedures to be adopted when applying for approval of thermostatic shower mixing valves.

Contents

1. General

2. Information Required

3. Example

4. Tests

5. Surveyors Report

6. Fees

Appendix A   List of Approved Thermostatic Shower Mixing Valves

1. General

Application for the approval of a thermostatic shower mixing valve should be made through a Marine Office to DSG1C Sunley House, all as indicated below.

2. Information Required

Full information should be provided by the manufacturer as follows:

.1 details of construction, including drawings;

.2 materials used, including any relevant certification;

.3 anticipated areas of use, including any constraints with regard to the type of water system in which the valve can be operated;

.4 installation, operation and maintenance instructions.

3. Example

A sample of the valve should be provided by the manufacturer.

.1 the valve should be permanently marked with the name and model number, and

.2 the off, hot and cold control positions, and

.3 the inlets should be marked hot and cold,

.4 all control knobs should be suitably marked to indicate their purpose.

4. Tests

All tests are to be undertaken at the manufacturers works, to the satisfaction of a surveyor and in accordance with the following:

.1 Three valves for tests are to be selected at random from the end of the production line store.

.2 A suitable rig will be required to allow testing as indicated below.

.3 Relevant records should be kept during tests for reference.

.4 The temperature of the hot water should be between 71°C and 77°C and should be recorded during each test.

.5 TEST 1

(i) The water pressures should be
HOT WATER—2.76 BAR (40 lbs per sq inch)
COLD WATER—2.76 BAR (40 lbs per sq inch)

(ii) With the valve in the fully open position (i.e. 'hot' position) the thermostat should be adjusted to give a shower water temperature of 40.5°C. ONCE THE THERMOSTAT HAS BEEN SET NO ADJUSTMENT SHOULD BE MADE FOR SUBSEQUENT TESTS.

(iii) The flow of water in litres per minute should be recorded.

(iv) The valve should be turned to the 'cold' position and the temperature of water recorded. The valve should be turned slowly from the 'cold' position to the 'hot' the temperature being recorded at each division on the scale. With the valve now fully open the cold water supply should be turned off and the shower water should cease to flow immediately.

(v) With the valve in the 'cold' position the control knob should be turned from 'cold' to 'hot' as quickly as possible. The temperature to which the shower water surges should be recorded together with the time in seconds the temperature is in excess of 40.5°C. Record final temperature of shower water before embarking on next test.

(vi) Note—The maximum surge temperature is to be not more than 50°C for not more than one second and mixed water temperature should return to not more than 43°C within 4 seconds.

.6 TEST 2

   (i) The water pressures should be
       HOT WATER—1.38 BAR (20 lbs per sq inch)
       COLD WATER—1.38 BAR (20 lbs per sq inch)

   (ii) Procedure as at Test 1

.7 TEST 3

   (i) The water pressures should be
       HOT WATER—2.76 BAR (40 lbs per sq inch)
       COLD WATER—2.07 BAR (30 lbs per sq inch)

   (ii) Procedure as at Test 1

.8 TEST 4

   (i) The water pressures should be
       HOT WATER—2.76 BAR (40 lbs per sq inch)
       COLD WATER—1.38 BAR (20 lbs per sq inch)

   (ii) Procedure as at Test 1

.9 TEST 5

   (i) The water pressures should be
       HOT WATER—2.07 BAR (30 lbs per sq inch)
       COLD WATER—0.69 BAR (10 lbs per sq inch)

   (ii) Procedure as at Test 1

.10 Reproducibility of results should be confirmed using different valves.

.5 Surveyors Report

The Surveyors report cross referencing all aspects of the application with comments as relevant should be attached to a MC 25/9 series file and submitted to Marine Directorate DSG1C.

6. Fees charged for consideration of an application for approval are dependent on Surveyor time spent plus expenses with regard to witnessing tests. A suitable deposit on fees is required before an application for approval can be progressed.

Appendix A

APPROVED THERMOSTATIC SHOWER MIXING VALVES

Name and Address of Manufacturer	Name of Valve	MDM No	Official Ref	Approval Expiry Date
Armitage Shanks Ltd Tubal Works Barrhead Glasgow G78 1NG	69354 AM 69364 AM	359/85	MC25/9/050	11.9.95
Barking-Grohe 1 River Road Barking Essex IG11 OHD	Neotherm No 35901	42/73	MC25/9/0220	1.1.95

Belco Manufacturing
  Co Ltd
241 City Road
London   EC1V
	Belco Junior A1 New
	  Protecta
		202/64	MC25/9/0104	1.1.95

Casa Buades s/g Eusebio Estade 79–80 PO Box 744 Palma de Mallorca Spain	M 20.122.00	310/86	MC25/9/0523	15.10.96
Dan Foss A/S DK 6430 Nordborg Denmark	TMC 153M	340/87	MC25/9/0169	3.9.97
Deltaflow Ltd Showell Road Busbury Wolverhampton	Temperfix Shower Mixing Valve	206/71	MC25/9/0199	1.1.95
Friedrich Grohe Arm,aturenfabrik 507 Hemer Postfach 260 West Germany	34.427 Grohmix ½") 34.604 Grohmix ½") 34.620 Grohmix ")	122/75	MC25/9/097	1.1.95
Meynell Valves Bushbury Wolverhampton WV10 9LB	Safemix Model SMIS	376/81	MC25/9/0143	1.1.95
Oras Oy Rauhankatu 28 26100 Rauma 10 Suomi Finland	M 180 000 Windsor M 675 M 184711 Oramix	 338/82 338/82	MC25/9/0443 MC25/9/0458	1.1.95 1.1.95
Toto Ltd 458 Shinozaki Kokura-Ku Kitakyushu 802 Japan	TM 4053 V	33/74	MC25/9/0197	1.1.95
Vargarda Armatur AB S-44700 Vargarda Sweden	Vaterm	155/79	MC25/9/0388	1.1.95
Walker Crossweller & Co Ltd Whaddom Works Cheltenham Gloucester GL52	Mira/Rada 722M Mira/Rada 15A, 15B, 15Z, 15ZA, 15BA, 15K and 15BK Mira/Rada 723L	167/78 218/80 282/86	MC25/9/0204 MC25/9/0204 MC25/9/0244	1.1.95 1.1.95 24.6.96

Survey of Crew Accommodation

Outline of Procedures

1. Plans, provided by the Owners/Builders, of the crew accommodation arrangements are to be examined by a Surveyor and/or in company with an Owners representative the crew accommodation is to be surveyed by a Surveyor.

2. Arrangements, equipment and materials which do not comply with the Regulations are to be identified and the Owners advised, in writing, as relevant.

3. Any proposals made for meeting the Regulations should be considered by the Surveyor and implemented where agreed.

4. Where the Regulations can not practically be met requirements to ensure that the overall provisions can be considered as 'no less favourable than those that would result from the full application of the regulation' should be discussed and the related exemptions from the Regulations to be applied for should be agreed with the Owners, noting that:—

    .1 Many owners at this stage consult directly with the relevant seafarers unions or organisations with a view to establishing that they have 'no objections' to the proposed exemptions,

    .2 if this procedure is not followed then the Surveyor should advise the Owners that in considering any proposed exemption from the Regulations, in accordance with the requirements of the ILO Conventions, the seafarers unions will be consulted by the Department.

    .3 At this time any particular unions or organisations should be identified as relevant to such a consultation procedure.

5. Where exemptions are found necessary the Surveyor should:

    .1 Obtain from the Owners, in writing, their formal application for such exemptions from particular Regulations, supported by their confirmation that any conditions associated with the proposed exemption(s) will be complied with together with the written agreement of the relevant Seafarers unions/organisation where they have been consulted directly.

    .2 Submit through Marine Directorate DSG1c a suitably completed 'Exemptions Sought' SUR 184 form together with the relevant supporting documentation and information, which should include a minute on file supporting or otherwise the Owners application for exemption(s).

6. Where consultation with the Seafarers unions/organisations has not taken place it will be put in hand by Marine Directorate DSG1c.

7. Given satisfactory consultations and completion of the survey a record of exemptions granted indicating any associated conditions will be issued through Marine Directorate DSG1c (Form SUR 185).

NB. Procedural details may be varied where justifiable in particular cases. *For survey of ships intended for transfer to the UK Register see also Annex 5.*

Transfer of ships to the United Kingdom Register

1.   The Department has in the past examined, with the industry and the maritime unions, the problems which arise and the costs which are incurred in improving crew accommodation to meet current standards when transferring ships to the United Kingdom register. The arrangements to minimise the burden of these requirements, wherever possible, were also considered. This Annex sets out the results of this examination and the Department's instructions in this matter.

2.   It is recognised that problems can arise when ships transfer registration.

3.   A ship coming on to the UK register is required to comply with Part I of the Regulations as amended. These Regulations give effect to International Conventions (International Labour Organisation No 68 (1946) and No 92 (1949), and the Supplementary Convention No 133 adopted at the 55th (1970) (Maritime) session of the International Labour Conference) which the United Kingdom has ratified. These regulations are supplemented in matters of detail by the Department's 'Instructions to Surveyors'.

4.   The requirement in the Regulations that an existing ship coming on to the UK register must comply with the Regulations as if it were a new ship is derived from the Convention and was also contained in previous Crew Accommodation Regulations. The 1978 Regulations and these 'Instructions to Surveyors' go somewhat further than the Convention in that they contain some requirements not specified in the Convention which reflect the higher living standards generally now prevailing.

5.   In order to facilitate the transfer of ships to the UK register, greater use of the provisions for exemption contained in Section 20(4) of the Merchant Shipping Act 1970 may be agreed as necessary. Accordingly when a ship repairer or owner makes application for the survey of crew accommodation the surveyor appointed to the ship should advise them, in writing, that the regulations are written in general terms and cover ships of all types and sizes and that they should indicate where they cannot comply and seek exemptions.

6.   The seafarers' unions have a legitimate interest in the matter of exemptions and the Department intends to consult fully with them before granting exemptions. There is no reason why an owner should not approach the seafarers' union concerned directly in order to seek a solution to the problems involved in complying with the regulations. The

Directorate is prepared to accept these agreed solutions if they deal with the social aspects of the regulations, but in matters affecting health and safety a surveyor should ensure that the solution is in keeping with the Directorate's recommendations and practice as indicated in these Instructions. A surveyor should list the problems involved in complying with the Regulations for the reference of those concerned.

7.   In the examination with the industry and the maritime unions referred to, a number of recurring problems were reviewed. The following paragraphs outline the way the Department has agreed to deal with these problems in ships transferring to the UK flag. They are also intended as a guide to surveyors as to the approach to adopt in those areas not included in these Instructions. When a surveyor accepts a particular construction, arrangement or equipment in keeping with the spirit and general guidance of this Annex his decision (which should be reported in due course) will, other than in the most exceptional circumstances, be supported by Marine Directorate Headquarters.

(1)   SHOWER FITTINGS (Regulation 28(17))

A surveyor may accept a mixing valve of the thermostatic type not approved by the Department provided he is satisfied that the temperature of the water meets the regulations, the valve will fail safe when the cold water supply is interrupted and warning notices are provided advising users against the dangers of scalding. Mixing valves which are not of the thermostatic type will continue to be accepted if the supply of hot and cold water is capable of being adjusted to meet the temperature requirements, the means of adjustment is tamper-proof and antiscald notices are displayed.

(2)   CARPETS (Regulation 10(4))

The provision of carpets is primarily a matter for resolution between owner and unions concerned. The Department for its part is prepared to accept, in lieu of a fitted carpet, one that covers a substantial area of the floor if provision is made to prevent it slipping. Where an existing carpet has not been type accepted by the Department a surveyor may nevertheless accept the carpet if he is reasonably satisfied that it has been tested to standards comparable to those laid down by the Department.

(3)   HOSPITALS (Regulation 35)

A surveyor should consult owners and unions before requiring changes to accommodation, furniture, ventilation or equipment. He may, at his discretion, postpone structural alterations, such as the widening of entrances, until the next scheduled dry docking.

(4) MEDICAL CABINET (Regulation 36)

The Department requires compliance with this Regulation on transfer.

(5) GALLEY EQUIPMENT (Regulation 32)

The type of equipment, size and function will vary from ship to ship and between different owners. A surveyor should consult owners and unions and on the basis of their joint agreement determine the extent to which exemptions may be considered necessary. Wherever practicable the provision of suitable equipment or structural alterations may be postponed until the next scheduled dry docking.

(6) MARKING (Regulation 20)

The physical marking of sleeping rooms or other spaces in the crew accommodation may be postponed until the next scheduled dry docking, but plans should show the intended allocation.

(7) VENTILATION (Regulation 16)

In the case of a ship the keel of which was laid or which was at a similar stage of construction before 1 July 1979 a surveyor should consult owners and unions and on the basis of their agreement determine the extent to which exemptions may be considered. The Department would however require as a minimum full compliance with paragraph 9 of Schedule 6 of the Regulations. In the case of a new ship the ventilation should generally be in accordance with the standards required by this regulation.

(8) PANTRIES (Regulation 25(5))

A surveyor should consult with the owners and the unions before dealing with the creation of a pantry and/or its equipment.

(9) ACCESS AND ESCAPE ARRANGEMENTS (Regulation 11)

Where emergency means of escape require the fitting of crash panels or fixed steel rungs on the outside of a structure in the vicinity of a suitable fully opening window the modifications may be postponed until the next scheduled dry docking. Given agreed temporary arrangements are provided and clearly indicated i.e. escape through areas not normally accepted, rope, portable ladders etc.

(10) ANTI-SYPHONIC VALVES (Regulation 18(1)(b))

In these 'Instructions to Surveyors' it is written (paragraph 2.14) that a single common waste line for drainage from washbasins, sinks, showers, scuppers and WCs may be accepted provided that each individual drainage pipe is fitted with an anti-syphonic vent so arranged as to eliminate the risk of seal breakage. The Department has no specification to cover anti-syphonic valves and provided they operate satisfactorily a surveyor should accept them without further reference. Where they are not fitted or are not effective a surveyor at his discretion may postpone compliance for a period not exceeding twelve months.

(11) VACUUM BREAKER (Regulation 29(7))

These 'Instructions to Surveyors' (paragraph 2.24.5) provides alternative arrangements to prevent the possible contamination of fresh water or drinking water when used for flushing water closets. If the existing arrangement does not comply it may be accepted by a surveyor, at his discretion, for a maximum period of twelve months.

(12) INSULATION (Regulations 6(2), 7(2) and (3))

Insulation required to meet the provision for noise reduction or thermal protection may at the surveyor's discretion be fitted at the next scheduled dry docking; provided heating arrangements are adequate.

(13) FURNITURE AND FITTINGS IN SLEEPING ROOMS (Regulation 23)

The provision of furniture and fittings in sleeping rooms is primarily a matter for the owner and the unions concerned and a surveyor should be guided by the agreement they reach.

(14) ACCOMMODATION LIGHTING (Regulation 15)

In the case of a ship the keel of which was laid or which was at a similar stage of construction on or after 1 July 1979 a surveyor may regard the provision of paragraph 8 of Schedule 6 as being of a sufficient standard.

(15) BEDS (Regulation 22)

The design and dimensions of a bed and mattress are primarily matters for the owner and the unions concerned and a surveyor should be guided by the agreement they reach.

INDEX

114

Printed in the United Kingdom for Her Majestys Stationery office
Dd 291329 4/89 C10 G443 10170